DRUG ABUSE: ESCAPE TO NOWHERE

DRUG ABUSE: ESCAPE TO NOWHERE

A Guide for Educators

Published by Smith Kline & French Laboratories, Philadelphia, in cooperation with the American Association for Health, Physical Education, and Recreation, a department of the National Education Association.

1967

CONTENTS

FOREWORD

"The young men of this land are not, as they are often called, a 'lost' race—they are a race that never yet has been discovered. And the whole secret, power, and knowledge of their own discovery is locked within them. . . ."

— Thomas Wolfe, The Web and the Rock

"I didn't think it could happen here." "I thought this was strictly a city problem." "I still don't believe it . . . not our kids." "What happened? . . . What did we do wrong?"

The place is Your Town. The problem, just discovered, is drug abuse.

Unfortunately, this scene will be repeated again and again in many communities . . . unless something is done to combat drug abuse *before* more young lives are twisted, irreparably and needlessly.

At this moment, no one knows just how extensive drug abuse by youngsters may be. But law enforcement and health officials close

9

to the situation agree that the problem is growing. What is also evident is that drug abuse is not limited to the slum areas of major cities: it can crop up anywhere . . . without reference to economic level, ethnic origin, intellectual or educational attainment, religious identity or social station. The world of drug abuse is a fraternity of the hopeless: anyone can join.

Educators face serious difficulties in combatting the problem. First, the sad fact is that many educators have had little or no resources with which to mount an effective drug abuse prevention program: useful materials on the subject have been scarce. Second, where programs have been initiated to combat drug abuse, they often have been hampered by inadequate or inaccurate information. And, finally, awareness of a drug abuse situation rarely occurs before some unfortunate incident exposes it. In essence, educators just haven't had the tools to do the job.

This Guide can help fill the information vacuum about drug abuse. Published by Smith Kline & French Laboratories, Philadelphia, in cooperation with the American Association for Health, Physical Education, and Recreation, a department of the National Education Association (AAHPER/NEA), this Guide is designed to provide educators with reliable information concerning drugs and other chemical products subject to abuse—and to suggest ways in which young people from elementary school through college can be reached on this vital subject. It is an information resource, not a plan for teaching. No single pedagogical technique will fit all learning situations about drug abuse. Instructors who become acquainted with the subject will find that candor, flexibility and situational perceptiveness are essential in teaching it.

SK&F's role in the preparation of this Guide is a logical outgrowth of the Company's responsibilities in manufacturing and distributing drug products. As SK&F is a leading producer of amphetamine and barbiturates, it has amassed considerable knowledge concerning the use of these drugs—and their abuse. To this knowledge has been added information gained in thousands of miles of travel for additional research with educators, law enforcement officials, physicians, pharmacists, students and drug abusers themselves. In the preparation of the manuscript, the good counsel of the AAHPER/NEA has proved invaluable, and in the review of this material, the authors have been fortunate in having the guidance of a distinguished panel of experts from education, medicine, pharmacy and law enforcement.

The Guide alone will not solve educational problems regarding drug abuse: only motivated educators, well informed and adequately supported by school authorities, can do something effective to prevent the problem. For education *is* the key to prevention—and truth concerning misuse of drugs is the best way prevention can be accomplished. To be sure, drug abuse can be considered a moral issue—but the battle to prevent it can never be successfully joined on that level alone. *Facts and positive motivation* are what young people need to help them make a sound decision should they one day face the pressure of "going along" with the drug abuse crowd.

Many behavioral scientists say drug abuse is a form of escape. You can help youth come to know it is an escape to nowhere.

ADVISORY PANEL

The subject of drug abuse has always been, and may long continue to be, one of considerable controversy. For this reason, it seemed imperative to have the advice of experts with experience in different professional disciplines. The material which follows, therefore, represents no single point of view. It is a synthesis of the best information now available, as modified and refined by the thinking of the following:

Harry J. Anslinger. U.S. Representative on the United Nations Commission on Narcotic Drugs. First United States Commissioner of Narcotics, 1930-1962. Chief U.S. Delegate to the Conference to Limit the Production of Opium, 1953. Observer, League of Nations Opium Advisory Committee, 1931-39. Delegate to the International Conference on the Suppression of Illicit Traffic in Narcotic Drugs, 1936. Author of numerous papers and books on narcotics.

Edward R. Bloomquist, M.D. Associate Clinical Professor of Surgery (Anesthesiology) at the University of Southern California School of Medicine, Los Angeles. Lecturer, Department of Police Sciences, California State College, Los Angeles. Member of various advisory committees for medical and law enforcement professions at Federal, state and local levels. Member of the Committee on Narcotics and Alcoholism of the American Medical Association's Council on Mental Health, 1964-65.

Henry Brill, M.D. Vice-Chairman of the New York State Narcotic Addiction Control Commission. Currently on leave as Director of Pilgrim State Hospital, West Brentwood, Long Island,

N.Y. Associate Editor of *The Psychiatric Quarterly*. Member of the National Research Council's Committee on Narcotic Addiction. Member of the Committee on Narcotics and Alcoholism of the American Medical Association's Council on Mental Health. Member of the Food and Drug Administration's Committee on Sedative, Stimulating and Hallucinogenic Drugs. Fellow of the American Psychiatric Association.

Michael N. Canlis. Sheriff and Coroner, County of San Joaquin, California. First Vice-President of the California Peace Officers Association. Member of the California Board of Corrections. Member, National Advisory Council on Police Training and Education.

James Fox, Ph.D. Acting Chief, Center for the Study of Narcotic and Drug Abuse, National Institute of Mental Health, Bethesda, Maryland. Director, Division of Drug Studies and Statistics, Bureau of Drug Abuse Control, Food and Drug Administration.

George P. Hager, Ph.D. Dean and Professor of Medicinal Chemistry, University of North Carolina School of Pharmacy. President of the Academy of Pharmaceutical Sciences of the American Pharmaceutical Association. President, 1965-66, and Vice-President, 1964-65, of the American Association of Colleges of Pharmacy. Member of the Mayor's Narcotics Committee, City of Minneapolis, 1965-66. Member, Ad Hoc Panel on Narcotic Addiction and Drug Abuse for the Office of Science and Technology, Washington, D.C., 1962-63.

Mrs. Jessie Kennedy. Principal of Northwestern High School, Detroit, Michigan. Former assistant principal, high school counselor and classroom teacher. Member of the Subcommittee on Police-Community Relations of the Citizens Committee for Equal Opportunity. Member, Planning Committee for Study of Educational Needs and Resources, Wayne County Interdepartmental School District. Member, Detroit Area Friends of Synanon.

John C. Krantz, Jr., Ph.D. Director of Scope, U.S. Pharmacopoeia, Towson, Maryland. Professor and Head of the Pharmacology Department, School of Medicine, University of Maryland, 1935-65. Co-author with C. J. Carr, of *Pharmacologic Principles of Medical Practice*, 6th Edition, Williams & Wilkins, Baltimore, 1965.

Edward Mileff, Ed.D. Consultant in Health and Safety Education for the American Association for Health, Physical Education, and Recreation, Washington, D.C. Staff Liaison to AAHPER's divisions of Health Education and Safety Education. Staff Liaison to the Joint Committee on Health Problems in Education of the National Education Association and the American Medical Association. Associate Professor of Health Education at San Diego State College, California, 1960-65.

Ruth E. Neumann. Teacher of health and physical education at White Bear Lake High School, Minnesota. Former counselor to high school students. Member of the American Association for Health, Physical Education, and Recreation.

Einar A. Olsen, Ed.D. Professor and Chairman of the Department of Health Education, Mankato State College, Minnesota. Member of the Executive Board of the American Association for Advancement of Instruction in Alcohol and Narcotics. Director at Large for the Minnesota Health and Tuberculosis Association. Co-author with C. A. Bucher and C. E. Willgoose of *Foundation of Health*, Appleton - Century - Crofts, New York, 1965.

This Guide was prepared as part of Smith Kline & French Laboratories' program in the area of drug abuse education. The program is headed by Donald K. Fletcher, Manager of Distribution Protection at SK&F.

The SK&F editorial staff for this Guide was: Mitchell Winn, Project Editor; Alvin M. Chester, Melmon May, Jr., and Margueritta R. Sutton.

PART I:
A HISTORICAL PERSPECTIVE

"I knew that for every hour of comparative ease and comfort its treacherous alliance might confer upon me now, I must endure days of bodily suffering; but I did not, could not, conceive the mental hell into whose fierce corroding fires I was about to plunge."

Thus, a young English immigrant, William Blair, described his experiences with opium in the July, 1842, issue of *The Knickerbocker*, a New York magazine.

His account—which was far from the first to describe the agonies of opium addiction—had little, if any, impact on the American public. Americans remained essentially ignorant of the addicting properties of opium and other narcotics till nearly the end of the 19th Century. By then, the fact of addiction was inescapable: over 100,000 Americans—and possibly as many as a million—were in some degree addicted to opium or its derivatives. A widely publicized estimate put the number of addicts in the general population at one in 400—about 190,000 people.

How It Happened

Drugs that affect behavior have been known since antiquity. Even people of the Stone Age may have been familiar with opium, hashish and cocaine. Primitive people used these drugs to induce states of intoxication during religious rites or, in the case of hashish, to prepare warriors for battle. As far back as 2700 B.C., marihuana was known to the Chinese emperor Shen Neng and recommended for gout, constipation and "absent-mindedness," among other uses. And in 500 B.C., the Scythians were reported by the Greek author Herodotus to be using the drug.

The most important of these drugs from a medical standpoint—opium—was known to the Egyptians by 1500 B.C. During the Greco-Roman period, opium was an economically and medically important drug, used for its sleep-inducing and pain-relieving (analgesic) properties. By the beginning of the Christian era, its use as a medicament had spread to other parts of Europe. It was administered for cough and diarrhea, as well as to reduce pain and induce sleep—good medical usage even today. In Renaissance Europe, opium also was used to treat hysteria, thus becoming one of the first therapeutic agents for a mental disorder.

Opium has also been used since earliest times for a quite different purpose—as an agent of indulgence. Opium (and its derivatives) has the power to allay anxiety, gloom and despair, as well as to provide escape from boredom and loneliness—even from reality itself. There is an apparent reference to opium in Homer's *Odyssey*, written in the 9th Century B.C. Rouse's translation tells of "a drug potent against pain and quarrels and charged with the forgetfulness of all trouble; whoever drank this mingled in the bowl, not one tear would he let fall the whole day long, not if mother and father should die, not if they should slay a brother or a dear son before his face and he should see it with his own eyes."

Both as a medicine and as a drug of indulgence, opium use spread throughout the world. By the 18th Century, opium was known in the American colonies where it was used by physicians as a therapeutic agent. In the latter part of the 18th Century, doctors recommended opium as a pain reliever in venereal disease, cancer, gallstones and dysentery. Its use was also advocated for relief of simple diarrhea, vomiting, spasms accompanying tetanus, and the pains of menstruation and childbirth. Benjamin Rush, an eminent

Philadelphia physician (and also a signer of the Declaration of Independence), used opium in typhus fever and recommended it "in all those fevers where wine (is) safe or proper." In a lecture at the University of Pennsylvania in 1791, Dr. Rush said he "observed the happiest effects from it in the fevers of the military hospitals of the United States during the late war."

Opium was also prescribed as a topical agent—applied to the abdomen to relieve spasms of the stomach, or to the cheek for relief of toothache. In addition, there were countless other 18th Century medical uses for the drug—many of which are still medically sound today.

Despite its wide medical use, opium's addictive liability was not understood by the medical profession. This lack of recognition is demonstrated by two medical theses of the 1790's. In one of them—the earliest M.D. thesis on opium from the University of Pennsylvania—Hast Handy in 1791 compared the actions of opium to liquor (then thought to be a stimulant) and found them similar. "Why, then," he asked, "may we not annex the term *stimulant* to opium?" Although Handy described in length the properties of opium, he never mentioned the possibility of addiction. A year later, Valentine Seaman, in his inaugural dissertation for an M.D. degree from the same university, stressed the dangers of opium in large quantities but failed to recognize the possibilities of addiction.

The problems of addiction arising from the spread of opium use were compounded in the 1800's by the discovery of two opium alkaloids, morphine (1805) and codeine (1832). The properties of these drugs, like those of their parent, were imperfectly understood. And even physicians who had come to recognize opium addiction as a medical fact failed to realize that these alkaloids were also dangerous. Consequently, morphine and codeine were administered to cure the opium habit—with the result that opium addicts were merely transferred from one addicting drug to another. Morphine became popular among opium users for another reason —its potency. One grain of morphine produces about the same effect as ten grains of opium.

But perhaps the most important factor influencing the spread of narcotic addiction was the invention, in 1843, of the hypodermic needle. Brought to this country in 1856, it was used widely during the Civil War to administer morphine, not only to battle-wounded, but also to those suffering from dysentery. Vast numbers of soldiers, according to later accounts, were returned to civilian life addicted to morphine. A term prevalent at the time, "Soldier's Illness," actually meant narcotic addiction. As morphine abuse spread in this country—it was not limited to the military population—the hypodermic needle gained in popularity as the means for administering the drug. In 1880, a physician, H. H. Kane, wrote: "Eighteen (patients) who came to me for treatment are using the drug subcutaneously. This means of using the drug is on the increase among habitués." And he added, "The danger of forming the habit from the use of the drug in this way is undoubted." Ten years later, Leslie E. Keeley, M.D., noted: "It has been stated that the greater proportion inject the solution subcutaneously by means of the hypodermic syringe, and my experience leads me to believe that this class is in the majority."

By the post Civil War era, there were several forms of opium and its derivatives—and many routes of administration. Opium was commonly taken orally in such forms as laudanum (a mixture corresponding to one grain of opium to 25 drops of alcohol), paregoric (one grain to 480 drops) and Dover's powder (opium mixed with ipecac and milk sugar). According to an account of the period, "Many of the old-fashioned habitués use the gum opium, but few paregoric, and a less number still, Dover's powder." Opium was also smoked, a practice introduced into San Francisco's Barbary Coast by Chinese after the California Gold Rush. Finally, pulverized opium was used in suppository form. Morphine was administered either orally (in forms similar to opium), rectally or hypodermically.

Since opium and its derivatives had important medical uses—and since these drugs could be bought legally and inexpensively in any pharmacy (and in many rural general stores)—they were found virtually everywhere. Alone or as components in pharmaceutical preparations or patent medicines, they were in use in homes across the country to provide relief from headache, diarrhea and even angina pectoris.

The final link in the opiate chain was forged in 1898 when a morphine derivative, heroin, was synthesized. Also initially considered non-addictive, heroin was available in many easily obtained pharmaceutical preparations and became a prime drug for treatment of morphine addiction. According to some sources, heroin created addicts by the thousands. Equally important, heroin firmly established the hypodermic needle as the instrument of drug abuse.

The Medical View

While addiction was mushrooming into a social problem during the 19th Century, the medical profession was becoming increasingly—though imperfectly—aware of this phenomenon. But controversy and uncertainty impeded concerted medical action. In *The Opium Habit*, published in 1868, writer Horace B. Day stated, "As yet the medical profession are by no means agreed as to the character or proper treatment of the opium disease."

The same writer also felt that opium did not affect all races alike—a view often expressed in medical writings of the day. He wrote that opium "seldom intoxicates the European; it seems habitually to intoxicate the Oriental. It does not generally distort the person of the English or American; in the East it is represented as frequently producing this effect."

Many physicians did not fully understand the dangers of opium. In 1881, Fred Heman Hubbard, M.D., wrote: "The effects of liquor or wine, as compared with those of opium, are coarse and brutalizing." And he also failed to recognize the problem of opium withdrawal: "They (opium users) dare not reduce the quantity taken, through fear of great suffering . . . when in reality no such results would follow, except in rare instances." As late as 1889, J. R. Black, M.D., writing in the *Cincinnati Lancet-Clinic*, recommended substituting the morphine habit for alcoholism. "The use of morphine," he wrote, "in place of alcohol is but a choice of evils, and by far the lesser."

Until the latter part of the century, the medical profession generally put opium abuse in the same category as alcohol abuse. Even those medical papers which inveighed strongly against opium did so in terms comparable to present-day writings against alcoholic beverages. In the nonmedical world there was a similar lack of distinction between the two forms of indulgence. An Englishman, Sir George Birdwood, writing in the *London Times* in 1883, described opium smoking as being "as harmless as twiddling your thumbs." In the same year, author John Liggins wrote, "Pro-opiumists maintain that opium smoking is no worse than gin and whiskey drinking."

The Opiate Users

In the 19th Century, opiate indulgence in America cut across economic and social lines, but was most prevalent among members of the middle and upper middle classes. The exception was opium smoking, associated with the top echelon of the underworld or with Chinese laborers imported to build railroads. But these opium smokers had little or no contact with the "opium eaters" of respectable society.

One writer described confirmed opium eaters as follows: "Professional and literary men, persons suffering from protracted nervous disorders, women obliged to work beyond their strength . . . maimed and shattered survivors from a hundred battlefields, diseased and disabled soldiers released from hostile prisons, anguished and hopeless wives and mothers . . ." Another writer found that "brilliant society ladies, zealous workers in good causes, literary toilers, and ambitious women have fallen beneath the witching power of morphia." He averred that narcotics use was increasing among "professional and business men and women" and that "at least two thirds of them belong to the better classes of society." Among the prominent persons of the 19th Century who abused opium without realizing its dangers were the American poet and author Edgar Allan Poe; the English poets Francis Thompson and Samuel Coleridge; and the Russian composer Modest Moussorgsky. Perhaps the most famous opium addict of the day was Thomas de Quincy, the author of *Confessions of an English Opium Eater.*

Toward the latter part of the century—as the magnitude of the problem was beginning to be realized—writers everywhere offered causal theories. Some blamed "the times," claiming the postwar era was one of increased tension and nervousness. Others blamed doctors, charging they prescribed narcotics indiscriminately. The latter charge was answered by a doctor who wrote, "If patients take up administration of narcotics at the point where the physician has ceased to prescribe them, and create in themselves the morphine habit, they have only themselves to blame." Whatever the initiating cause, it seems probable that most users turned to narcotics to escape physical or emotional pain, then gradually became addicted.

Change in Public Attitude

Throughout the 18th Century and most of the 19th Century,

the use of opiates—at least orally—was not generally offensive to public morals. Occasional use, as many of the foregoing quotes indicate, was held in much the same light as an occasional drink is today. And opium users themselves suffered little public condemnation, doubtless because of the social standing of so many of them. When people were known to be "enslaved by the habit" (the common term of the day), they were often more pitied than condemned. The drug itself was held to blame, not the user. Opium smokers, however, were held in low esteem because of the connection of smoking with the underworld and with Oriental "opium dens."

H. H. Kane, one of the 19th Century physicians who inveighed strongly against opium use, while maintaining a compassionate attitude toward addicts, wrote of "a curse that entangles in its hideous meshes such great men as William Blair, Robert Hall (a clergyman), John Randolph (American statesman) and William Wilberforce (English philanthropist and abolitionist)."

Thus, while there were varying degrees of denunciation against opium use, there was little against the user himself. The strongest warnings came from members of the medical profession—but even medicine's view was far from unanimous, though it tended to coalesce toward the end of the 19th Century. The general public was essentially apathetic—due to ignorance of the nature of narcotic addiction and its serious social implications. Some states had attempted to control narcotics use as early as 1862, but these efforts were sporadic and did not reflect widespread public concern.

By the 1890's, however, public attitudes toward narcotic use and users began to change. One reason was that many physicians now fully recognized the destructive nature of narcotic dependence and gave widespread publicity to their findings. Public awareness also came from addicts who wrote accounts of their experiences, and from newspapers which published sensational stories of addiction among young people. Added to these factors was the growing realization that great numbers of people had become addicted. By 1901, when both lay and professional groups were expressing alarm over the narcotics problem, a special committee of the American Pharmaceutical Association surveyed pharmacies to learn the extent of the public's demand for addiction-producing drugs. In its report, the group termed the problem "appalling."

As information—as well as misinformation—became widely available, attitudes toward addiction began to polarize, sparking the beginning of a controversy which has persisted to the present day. Some saw addiction as an illness. Others called it a vice. But, since the addict could still purchase drugs legally and secure assistance from doctors, little connection existed between addiction and criminal behavior. This association, however, was soon to appear.

Legal Controls

The first Federal attempt to control opium use came in 1909 with an act that prohibited the importation of opium, its preparations, and derivatives except for medical purposes. At lower levels, by 1912 many cities and every state but one had laws governing the prescribing and selling of opiates. In practice, though, these local and state laws were not vigorously enforced. Consequently, there was virtually no limitation on domestic sales of narcotics; people could still purchase opium, morphine, laudanum and other narcotics freely at pharmacies, without prescriptions.

Growing public concern over the magnitude of the narcotics problem, and realization that local and state laws were inadequate, led to the passage, by Congress, of the Harrison Act (1914). Significantly, this act did not make addiction illegal but sought to control the production, manufacture and distribution of narcotic drugs. The law required registration and payment of an occupational tax by all persons dealing with narcotic drugs. It further specified that only physicians could dispense narcotics, and that pharmacists could sell such drugs only on written prescription.

For the addict, even these restricted legal sources were soon eliminated. Because of the mood of the time, several court decisions subsequent to passage of the act had the effect of stringently limiting the role of physicians in prescribing narcotics to addicts. These decisions permitted physicians to dispense drugs to addicts in diminishing quantities to break drug habits, but not in quantities sufficient to *maintain* such habits. This fine legal distinction, plus overprescribing by some physicians, led to a number of physician arrests and convictions. Such legal problems, added to the near medical impossibility of treating addicts on an outpatient basis, soon caused doctors to stop treating addiction.

Outpatient clinic resources, established by local health departments on an experimental basis beginning in 1919, were not long available.

By 1923, some 40 special clinics were open throughout the country to dispense drugs to addicts as a part of treatment. But widespread allegations that the clinics were handing out drugs too freely, thus spreading addiction instead of curtailing it, led to their closing by Federal authorities that year. This action was supported by state and local authorities and by the House of Delegates of the American Medical Association.

Cut off from both legal drugs and clinic assistance, addicts unable to break their habits turned entirely to an underworld market that had been only a minor source of supply previously. To meet the high cost of black-market narcotics, addicts became increasingly involved in criminal activities. Naturally enough, the public soon linked opiate addiction and crime. The heroin addict, in particular, was stamped with the strongest opprobrium, probably due to his use of the hypodermic needle, a practice considered revolting by many people.

As the illegal traffic burgeoned, narcotics officials found that, in order to crush this traffic, it was necessary to crack down on addicts (often sources of supply) as well as non-addict pushers—through arrests and compulsory drug withdrawal in a controlled setting. Accordingly, Congress, in 1929, authorized construction of special high-security addiction treatment facilities at Lexington, Kentucky, and at Fort Worth, Texas. By World War II, international treaties, vigorous law enforcement, and expanded drug abuse education were credited with a reduction in the number of known addicts in the U.S. to less than 60,000 individuals.

After World War II, public concern about addiction surged again. Rapidly rising arrest rates disclosed that increasing numbers of younger people were becoming involved with narcotics. The reaction was to call for more stringent controls. Congress and state legislators complied by increasing penalties for narcotic offenses. For example, under the Narcotic Drug Control Act of 1956, the mandatory minimum penalty for a first violation of the Harrison Act (for illegal sale) was raised to 5 years with no possibility of probation or parole.

Other Voices

At the same time that stiffer penalties were being set, the view of the addict as a sick person began to have greater impact on popular opinion. This view was reinforced by sympathetic—if somewhat inaccurate—portrayals of addicts on television, in films, in books and magazines, and on the stage. In contrast to the accustomed view of the addict as a vicious criminal, these presentations showed the addict as a tortured human being, desperately in need of help.

A further impetus to a changing attitude among some segments of the population came with the White House Conference on Narcotics and Drug Abuse in 1962. The question was again raised: Is the addict a sick person or a criminal? In its report to the Conference delegates, the Ad Hoc Panel on Narcotic Addiction and Drug Abuse referred to the addict as "an inadequate personality . . . unable to cope with the stresses of normal life." From the debates and comments which followed the Conference, a new consensus emerged: The addict is a sick person, as well as a criminal. Out of the Conference also came heightened interest in the need for addict treatment. A number of state, municipal and nongovernmental programs were undertaken in various parts of the country.

Equally significant, perhaps, is that—while in no way minimizing the dangers of addiction, or the culpability of traffickers in narcotics—most law enforcement officers have come to regard the addict as a victim as well as a lawbreaker. Many law enforcement agencies now participate in educational programs designed to discourage drug abuse—particularly among young people.

Non-Narcotic Drug Abuse

In recent years, public attention has been increasingly focused on the abuse of non-narcotic drugs such as amphetamine (stimulants), barbiturates (sedatives), certain tranquilizers and "hallucinogens" such as LSD-25. The growing trend toward abuse of these drugs was noted by the 1962 White House Conference. Much of the awareness has come from newspaper and magazine articles reporting widespread abuse of non-narcotic drugs by high school and college youth. Though the extent of use is unknown, there is considerable evidence that the problem is growing. In 1966, the Medical Society of New York reported that, while drug abuse in the city's high schools or the state's colleges was not extensive, marihuana, LSD and similar drugs "may soon present a dangerous problem." The medical society report blamed this possibility, in part, on "frequent glorification of hallucinogens without adequate details regarding their danger."

24

Public opinion has tended to regard the non-narcotic abuser—except, perhaps, for the marihuana offender—with less harshness than the narcotic addict. In part, this may reflect the public's association of non-narcotic drugs with occasional or spree use, the social acceptance and widespread use of amphetamine and barbiturates in legitimate medical therapy, and the availability of such drugs from other than underworld contacts. Also, while the dangers of narcotic addiction are acknowledged, the dangers inherent in many non-narcotics have not been generally recognized.

The net result of this thinking has been to curtail misuse of non-narcotics by laws aimed at the *source* rather than the user. Accordingly, in 1965, proceeding from a recommendation by the President's Advisory Commission on Narcotic and Drug Abuse, the Drug Abuse Control Amendments were added to the Food, Drug and Cosmetic Act of 1938. The purpose of these Amendments was to eliminate illegal traffic in amphetamine, barbiturates and drugs of abuse other than narcotics and marihuana. To enforce these amendments, a Bureau of Drug Abuse Control has been created under the Food and Drug Administration (FDA) to regulate distribution of amphetamine, barbiturates and other abused non-narcotic drugs.

As for the abuser—and potential abuser—of non-narcotics, there is growing recognition of the value of an educational, rather than a punitive approach. This is reflected in a special function assigned to the Bureau of Drug Abuse Control—to institute educational programs—and in the statements of government officials. James L. Goddard, M.D., Commissioner of Food and Drugs, has stressed the role of the classroom teacher in the educational process: "We may provide the law enforcement, but *you* must provide the educational climate to eliminate drug abuse."

PART II:
DRUGS OF ABUSE AND THEIR EFFECTS

Substances with abuse potential range from simple kitchen spices through common flowers and weeds to highly sophisticated drugs. All these substances may be divided into five categories: 1) narcotics, 2) sedatives, 3) tranquilizers, 4) stimulants and 5) hallucinogens.

Medically defined, narcotics are drugs which produce insensibility or stupor due to their depressant effect on the central nervous system. Included in this definition are opium, opium derivatives (morphine, codeine, heroin) and synthetic opiates (meperidine, methadone). As regulated by Federal narcotic laws, however, the term "narcotics" also embraces the coca leaf and its derivative, cocaine. Pharmacologically, this drug is a stimulant, not a depressant, but for law enforcement purposes it is considered a narcotic. All other drugs susceptible to abuse are non-narcotics.*

---

*This includes marihuana. Popularly regarded as a narcotic drug, it is not so considered either medically or under law. The confusion, in part, stems from the fact that the drug is controlled by the Federal Bureau of Narcotics.

Whatever their classification, most of these drugs have important legitimate applications. Narcotic, sedative, tranquilizing and stimulant drugs are essential to the practice of modern medicine. Hallucinogens are used in medical research. To the abuser, though, these same medically useful drugs have a compelling attribute: they affect the nervous system, producing a change in his emotional responses or reactions. The abuser may feel intoxicated, relaxed, happy or detached from a world that is painful and unacceptable to him.

With repeated use, many drugs cause *physical dependence*. This is an adaptation whereby the body learns to live with the drug, tolerates ever-increasing doses, and reacts with certain withdrawal symptoms when deprived of it. The total reaction to deprivation is known clinically as an abstinence syndrome. The symptoms that appear depend on the amount and kind of drug used. Withdrawal symptoms disappear as the body once again adjusts to being without the drug—or if the drug is reintroduced.

With many drugs, the chronic user finds he must constantly increase the dose in order to obtain an effect equal to that from the initial dose. This phenomenon, called *tolerance*, represents the body's ability to adapt to the presence of a foreign substance. Tolerance does not develop for all drugs or in all individuals; but with drugs such as morphine, addicts have been known to build up great tolerance very quickly. It is interesting to note, however, that tolerance does not develop for all the possible effects of a given drug. For example, tolerance develops to the euphoric-like effects of heroin, but only slightly to the constricting effects on the pupil of the eye. *Complete* tolerance may not develop to a drug's toxic effects; accordingly, no matter how high his tolerance, an addict may still administer a lethal dose to himself. Tolerance can occur without physical dependence.

A more important factor in keeping the abuser enslaved by his habit is the *psychic* or *psychological dependence* present in most cases of drug abuse. Psychic dependence is an emotional or mental adaptation to the effects of the drug. The abuser not only likes the feeling from the drug and wants to reexperience it—he feels he cannot function normally without the drug. It enables him to escape from reality—from his problems and frustrations. The drug and its effects seem to provide the answer to everything, including disenchantment and boredom. With the drug, all seems well. It is the psychological factor which causes an addict who has been withdrawn from his physical dependence to return to drug abuse.

All substances with abuse potential can produce changes in behavior, particularly when large amounts are improperly used. The abuser may be withdrawn and solitary, or sociable and talkative. He may be easily moved to tears or laughter. He may be quick to argue or believe that "someone is out to get him." These changes in behavior may be harmless or may constitute a danger to both the abuser and society. Much of the public concern about drug abuse stems from widely publicized changes in behavior accompanying the use of drugs.

Three frequently confused terms encountered in drug abuse discussions are "addiction," "habituation" and "drug dependence." *Addiction* has been defined as a state of periodic or chronic intoxication produced by the repeated consumption of a drug and involves tolerance, psychological dependence, usually physical dependence, an overwhelming compulsion to continue using the drug, and detrimental effects on both the individual and society. *Habituation* has been defined as a condition, resulting from the repeated consumption of a drug, which involves little or no evidence of tolerance, some psychological dependence, no physical dependence, and a desire (but not a compulsion) to continue taking the drug for the feeling of well-being that it engenders. Detrimental effects, if any, are primarily on the individual.

Through the years, the terms addiction and habituation have frequently been used interchangeably—and erroneously so, with the result that discussions of drug abuse have been fraught with semantic difficulties. Accordingly, the World Health Organization (WHO) recently recommended that these terms be replaced by a single and more general term—"drug dependence." *Drug dependence* is described as "a state arising from repeated administration of a drug on a periodic or continuous basis." Since many different kinds of drugs can be involved in drug dependence, the term is further qualified in accordance with the particular drug being used: Examples: "drug dependence of the morphine type," "drug dependence of the barbiturate type."

Although it was hoped that the newer terminology involving "drug dependence" and its various qualifiers would eventually replace the older terms of "addiction" and "habituation," from a practical standpoint this is not possible. The language of laws (international, national and local) which governs drugs subject to abuse encompasses the terms "addiction" and "habituation." As it would be difficult to set these laws aside, it appears that all three terms will become a part of drug abuse terminology, with "drug dependence" being favored by medically oriented groups and "addiction" and "habituation" being favored in legislative and law enforcement circles.

MORPHINE-LIKE NARCOTICS (OPIATES)

Medical Use. Natural and synthetic morphine-like drugs are the most effective pain relievers in existence and are among the most valuable drugs available to the physician. They are widely used for short-term acute pain resulting from surgery, fractures, burns, etc., and in the latter stages of terminal illnesses such as cancer. Morphine is the standard of pain relief by which other narcotic analgesics are evaluated.

The depressant effect of opiates produces drowsiness, sleep and a reduction in physical activity. Side effects can include nausea and vomiting, constipation, itching, flushing, constriction of pupils and respiratory depression.

Manufacture and distribution of medicinal opiates are stringently controlled by the Federal government through laws designed to keep these products available only for legitimate medical use. One aspect of the controls is that those who distribute these products are registered with Federal authorities and must comply with specific record-keeping and drug security requirements.

Abuse. The appeal of morphine-like drugs lies in their ability to reduce sensitivity to both psychological and physical stimuli and to produce a sense of euphoria. These drugs dull fear, tension or anxiety. Under the influence of morphine-like narcotics, the addict is usually lethargic and indifferent to his environment and personal situation. For example, a pregnant addict will usually continue drug abuse despite the fact that her baby will likewise be addicted—and probably die shortly after birth unless medical treatment is undertaken at once.

The price tag on the abuse of these drugs is high. Chronic use may lead to both physical and psychological dependence. Psychological dependence is the more serious of the two, since it is still operative after drug use has been discontinued. With chronic use, tolerance develops and ever-increasing doses are required in order to achieve a desired effect. As the need for the drug increases, the addict's activities become increasingly drug-centered. When drug supplies are cut off, characteristic withdrawal symptoms may develop.

Symptoms of withdrawal from narcotic analgesics include:
- Nervousness, anxiety, sleeplessness.
- Yawning, running eyes and nose, sweating.
- Enlargement of the pupils, "gooseflesh," muscle twitching.
- Severe aches of back and legs, hot and cold flashes.
- Vomiting and diarrhea.
- Increase in breathing rate, blood pressure and temperature.
- A feeling of desperation and an obsessional desire to secure a "fix."

The intensity of withdrawal symptoms varies with the degree of physical dependence. This, in turn, is related to the amount of drug customarily used. Typically, the onset of symptoms occurs about 8-12 hours after the last dose. Thereafter, symptoms increase in intensity, reach a peak between 36-72 hours, and then gradually diminish over the next 5-10 days. However, weakness, insomnia, nervousness, and muscle aches and pains may persist for several weeks. In extreme cases, death may result.

Because increasing pressure by law enforcement authorities has made traffic in heroin more difficult, "street" supplies have tended to contain increasingly low percentages of active ingredient. (The heroin content of a "bag" now ranges between 3 and 10%. Pure heroin is "cut"—diluted—with milk sugar.) As a consequence, many present-day narcotic addicts experience relatively mild withdrawal symptoms unless they are consuming many bags per day. On the other hand, narcotic addicts can die from overdosage when the supplies they buy in the "street" contain more than the customary low percentage of heroin. (Addict deaths from over-dosage at a rate of one a day have been reported in New York City.)

Exempt Narcotic Preparations

Under Federal law, some preparations containing small amounts of narcotics are exempt from the prescription requirement. The reason for their exemption lies in the fact that very large quantities of such preparations would have to be consumed regularly for a considerable time to produce significant dependence. These products include certain cough medicines and paregoric remedies which may be sold in pharmacies without a doctor's prescription. Pharmacists selling exempt preparations must have a Federal narcotics stamp.

Paregoric: Medical Use. Paregoric, a liquid preparation containing an extract of opium, is used to counteract diarrhea and to relieve abdominal pain.

Cough Syrup: Medical Use. Exempt cough formulas which contain codeine are used to combat the symptoms of respiratory disorders. While the chief use of codeine is for pain relief, it is also an effective cough suppressant when taken in small doses.

Abuse. Although these preparations are reasonably safe and free of addiction liability when used as directed, they can be abused. Addicts will sometimes turn to paregoric or cough syrups—as well as other drugs—when heroin is in short supply. (Very large quantities of these exempt preparations are consumed by addicts when abused as inferior substitutes for more potent drugs.)

In some areas, high school students are known to abuse paregoric medicines and codeine cough remedies. Of the formulas which have been abused, a number have a high alcohol content—which very probably has much to do with their popularity. (The alcohol content in some of these products is as high as 40%.)

DEPRESSANTS (SEDATIVES)

This group includes a variety of old and new drugs which have a depressant effect on the nervous system. Within this group, the most commonly abused products are the barbiturates. The "street" term for this type of product is "goofball."

Medical Use. The first barbituric acid derivative, barbital, was introduced to medicine shortly after the turn of the century. Since that time, over 2500 barbiturates have been synthesized. Today, only about 30 are widely used medically. The barbiturates are among the most versatile depressant drugs available. They are used for epilepsy, high blood pressure, insomnia and in the treatment and diagnosis of mental disorders. They are used before and during surgery. Alone or in combination with other drugs, they are prescribed for almost every kind of illness or special situation requiring sedation. Used under medical supervision, barbiturates are impressively safe and effective.

Abuse. The abuser takes barbiturates orally, intravenously or rectally. Although barbiturate intoxication closely resembles alcoholic intoxication, barbiturate abuse is far more dangerous than alcohol abuse or even narcotic abuse. Unintentional overdosage can easily occur. Convulsions, which may follow withdrawal, can be fatal. Overindulgence in alcohol before barbiturate ingestion may result in fatal depression of respiratory and cardiovascular systems.

The barbiturate abuser exhibits slurred speech and staggering gait. His reactions are sluggish. He is emotionally erratic and may be easily moved to tears or laughter. Frequently, he is irritable and antagonistic. Sometimes, he has impressions of euphoria. Because he is prone to stumble or drop objects, he often is bruised and has cigarette burns.

Chronic misuse of barbiturates is accompanied by the development of tolerance and both psychological and physical dependence. Physical dependence appears to develop only with continued use of doses much greater than those customarily used in the practice of medicine. In a physically dependent barbiturate abuser, abrupt withdrawal is extremely dangerous. Withdrawal from the drug should *always* be supervised by a physician.

In withdrawal, during the first 8-12 hours after the last dose, the barbiturate abuser who has become physically dependent appears to improve. After this, there are signs of increasing nervousness, headache, anxiety, muscle twitching, tremor, weakness, insomnia, nausea and a sudden drop in blood pressure when the person stands abruptly (he often faints). These symptoms are quite severe at about 24 hours. There are changes in the electroencephalographic readings and, within 36-72 hours, convulsions resembling epileptic seizures may develop. Such convulsions occasionally occur as early as the sixteenth hour of withdrawal or as late as the eighth day.

Convulsions, which can be fatal, are an ever-present danger with barbiturate withdrawal and distinguish barbiturate from narcotic withdrawal. (Narcotic addiction is not characterized by a failure of muscular coordination or by convulsions upon drug withdrawal.) Whether or not convulsions occur, there may be a period of mental confusion. Delirium and hallucinations similar to the delirium tremens (DT's) of alcoholism may develop. Delirium may be accompanied by an extreme agitation that contributes to exhaustion. The delirium may persist for several days followed by a long period of sleep. (Delirium may also develop early in the course of withdrawal.)

Miscellaneous Depressants

A number of nonbarbiturate depressants used medically to induce sleep and for sedation are also capable of being abused. With chronic use of high doses, tolerance, physical dependence and psychological dependence can develop. Withdrawal phenomena occur following abrupt discontinuation of drug use. Clinical symptoms and patterns of abuse resemble those observed for barbiturates.

Because of their abuse potential, several of these drugs have become subject to the regulations of the Drug Abuse Control Amendments of 1965. Glutethimide, ethchlorvynol, ethinamate and methyprylon are examples of the newer sedatives which are now controlled.

TRANQUILIZERS

The term "tranquilizer" refers to a rather large group of drugs introduced since the early 1950's. Unlike barbiturate-type sedatives, tranquilizers can be used to counteract tension and anxiety without producing sleep or significantly impairing mental and physical function.

All tranquilizers are not alike. In general, they may be divided into two groups—"major" or "minor"—based on their usefulness in severe mental disorders (psychoses). "Major" tranquilizers are those with antipsychotic activity. These include primarily the phenothiazine and reserpine-type drugs. Reserpine also is used to treat high blood pressure. The antipsychotic tranquilizers are not known to produce physical dependence. Abuse of this type of tranquilizer is practically nonexistent.

The "minor" group of tranquilizers includes a number of chemically quite different drugs. For the most part, they are not effective in psychotic conditions. They are widely used, however, in the treatment of emotional disorders characterized by anxiety and tension. Many are useful as muscle relaxants.

Through the years, it has been found that some members of this second group of tranquilizers occasionally have been abused. The two drugs most often reported have been meprobamate and chlordiazepoxide. Chronic abuse of these drugs, involving increasingly larger daily doses, may result in the development of physical and/or psychological dependence. Symptoms during misuse and following abrupt withdrawal closely resemble those seen with barbiturates. Chronic use of high doses can result in convulsions if the drugs are suddenly withdrawn. In order to combat abuse of this category of tranquilizers, the FDA has requested more stringent controls on meprobamate, chlordiazepoxide and diazepam. To date, abuse of tranquilizers has been infrequent and has not become a "street" problem. Abuse supplies usually are obtained by having prescriptions refilled in excess of normal needs.

STIMULANTS

This group includes drugs which directly stimulate the central nervous system. The most widely known stimulant in this country is caffeine, an ingredient of coffee, tea, cola and other beverages. Since the effects of caffeine are relatively mild, its usage is socially acceptable and not an abuse problem. The synthetic stimulants such as amphetamine and other closely related drugs are more potent and can be abused. Another dangerous stimulant is cocaine.

Cocaine

Cocaine is obtained from the leaves of the coca bush found in certain South American countries. It is an odorless, white crystalline powder with a bitter taste, producing numbness of the tongue. (The word "coca" is often confused with "cacao." The two are not related. Cacao is the name of a tree from which cocoa and chocolate are derived.)

Medical Use. Cocaine was once widely used as a local anesthetic. Its place in medicine, however, has been largely taken by newer, less toxic drugs.

The stimulant effect of cocaine results in excitability, talkativeness and a reduction in the feeling of fatigue. Cocaine may produce a sense of euphoria, a sense of increased muscular strength, anxiety, fear and hallucinations. Cocaine dilates the pupils and increases the heartbeat and blood pressure. Stimulation is followed by a period of depression. In overdosage, cocaine may so depress respiratory and heart function that death results.

Abuse. International control measures have greatly reduced the abuse of cocaine, although the chewing of coca leaves in some South American countries is still common. Cocaine is either sniffed or injected directly into a vein. The abuse of cocaine tends to be more sporadic than the abuse of heroin. The intense stimulatory effects usually result in the abuser voluntarily seeking sedation. This need for sedation has given rise to a practice of combining a depressant drug such as heroin with a drug such as cocaine ("speed-ball") or alternating a drug such as cocaine with a depressant. In some persons, cocaine produces violent behavior. Cocaine does not produce physical dependence. Tolerance does not develop and abusers seldom increase their customary dose. When drug supplies are cut off, the cocaine user does not experience withdrawal symptoms, but he does feel deeply depressed and hallucinations may persist for some time. Strong psychological dependence on the drug and a desire to reexperience the intense stimulation and hallucinations cocaine produces lead to its chronic misuse.

Amphetamine

Medical Use. Amphetamine has been available since the early 1930's. First used medically as a nasal vasoconstrictor in treatment of colds and hay fever, amphetamine was later found to stimulate the nervous system. This stimulating activity is the primary basis for its uses in medicine today. Amphetamine is used for narcolepsy (a disease characterized by involuntary attacks of sleep) and to counteract excessive drowsiness caused by sedative drugs. But in the main, amphetamine is used in obesity, where the drug exerts an anti-appetite effect, and to relieve mild depression such as that accompanying menopause, convalescence, grief and senility. Paradoxically, this drug tends to calm hyperactive, noisy, aggressive children, thus producing more normal behavior.

Amphetamine may produce a temporary rise in blood pressure, palpitations, dry mouth, sweating, headache, diarrhea, pallor and dilation of the pupils. Such effects are generally seen only with high doses or as occasional side effects with therapeutic doses. Amphetamine drugs seldom cause death, even in acute overdosage.

Abuse. Amphetamine is a stimulant. It increases alertness, dispels depression and superimposes excitability over feelings of fatigue.

It also produces an elevation of mood and a feeling of well-being. All these are factors underlying amphetamine abuse—and explain its popular name, "pep pill."

Amphetamine usually is taken orally in the form of tablets or capsules. However, there have been reports of intravenous use in which amphetamine is dissolved in water and then injected. With this route of administration, the effects of the drug are felt almost immediately.

Most medical authorities agree that amphetamine does not produce physical dependence, and there is no characteristic abstinence syndrome upon abrupt discontinuation of drug use. Mental depression and fatigue, however, are frequently experienced after the drug has been withdrawn. Psychological dependence is common and is an important factor in continuance of and relapse to amphetamine abuse. The development of tolerance permits the use of many times the usual therapeutic dose.

An acute psychotic episode may occur with intravenous use, or a drug psychosis may develop with the chronic use of large doses. Symptoms include extreme hyperactivity, hallucinations and feelings of persecution. These bizarre mental effects usually disappear after withdrawal of the drug.

Generally, misuse is associated with milder symptoms. The abuser is talkative, excitable and restless, and experiences a "high." He suffers from insomnia, perspires profusely, has urinary frequency and exhibits a tremor of the hands.

Miscellaneous Stimulants

There are a number of other stimulant drugs which, while not closely related to amphetamine chemically, do have similar uses and effects. (A typical drug of this type is phenmetrazine, used medically in the treatment of obesity.)

When abused, such drugs can produce all of the effects associated with the abuse of amphetamine, including hallucinations. Nevertheless, such drugs are not as widely misused as amphetamine drugs, and only phenmetrazine has been placed under the same controls imposed upon amphetamine.

HALLUCINOGENS

Distortions of perception, dream images and hallucinations are characteristic effects of a group of drugs variously called hallucinogens, psychotomimetics, dysleptics or psychodelics. These drugs include mescaline, d-lysergic acid diethylamide (LSD), psilocybin and dimethyltryptamine (DMT). At present, they have no general clinical medical use—except for research applications. However, they are being encountered with increasing frequency as drugs of abuse.

Marihuana, while chemically distinct from the foregoing, is also considered a hallucinogen. Pharmacologically, it is *not* a narcotic although its control under the Marihuana Tax Act of 1937—and later laws—is somewhat similar to the control imposed on narcotics. Also, like narcotic law enforcement, marihuana law enforcement is handled by the Federal Bureau of Narcotics as well as certain state and local law enforcement agencies.

Marihuana (Cannabis)

According to the Commission on Narcotic Drugs of the Economic and Social Council of the United Nations, marihuana abuse is more widespread, from a geographical standpoint, than abuse of any other dangerous drug. Widely encountered in North and South America, Africa, Southeast Asia and the Middle East, it is known as bhang or ganja in India, hashish in the Middle East, dagga in South Africa and maconha or djamba in South America.

The intoxicating substance which gives marihuana its activity is found primarily in a resin from the flowering tops and leaves of the female plant. The potency of marihuana varies with the geographical location in which the plant grows, time of harvest, and the plant parts used. For example, hashish is stronger than American marihuana because the former contains more resin.

Medical Use. At one time, marihuana had a minor place in the practice of medicine. But because the safety and effectiveness of newer drugs so outweigh the limited utility of marihuana, it is no longer considered medically respectable in the United States. In a few countries of the world (such as India and Pakistan), it still may be encountered as a local remedy.

Abuse. Marihuana may be smoked, sniffed or ingested, but effects are experienced most quickly with smoking. The mental effects include a feeling of euphoria, exaltation and a dreamy sensation accompanied by a free flow of ideas. Senses of time, distance, vision and hearing are distorted. Sometimes panic and fear are experienced. Hallucinations may develop with large doses. In the company of others, the marihuana user is talkative and laughs easily. When alone, he is more often drowsy and quiet. The initial period of stimulation is frequently followed by a moody reverie and drowsiness. The user's ability to perform many tasks normally or safely—particularly automobile driving—is seriously impaired.

Other effects of marihuana include dizziness, dry mouth, dilated pupils and burning eyes, urinary frequency, diarrhea, nausea and vomiting, and hunger, particularly for sweets.

Marihuana does not produce physical dependence or an abstinence syndrome. Once the user has established the amount of marihuana needed to achieve his particular "high," there is little tendency to increase the dose, indicating that tolerance doesn't develop. Moderate to strong psychic dependence can develop in accordance with the user's appreciation of the drug's effects.

In terms of some effects on behavior, use of marihuana is roughly comparable to moderate abuse of alcohol (also a drug). Like alcohol, it tends to loosen inhibitions and increase suggestibility, which explains why an individual under the influence of marihuana may engage in activities he would not ordinarily consider. Although the marihuana smoker sometimes feels himself capable of extraordinary physical and mental feats, he seldom acts to accomplish them for fear of disrupting his "euphoric" state. But what he does not realize is that the drug can have unpredictable effects—even on persons accustomed to its use.

To date, available information indicates that marihuana has few detrimental effects on an individual's *physical* health. Psychic dependence and the drug's effects, however, may lead to extreme lethargy, self-neglect and preoccupation with use of marihuana to a degree that precludes constructive activity. Additionally, the use of marihuana may precipitate psychotic episodes or cause impulsive behavior in reaction to fear or panic. According to a 1965 report on drug dependence in the Bulletin of the World Health Organization: "Abuse of cannabis (marihuana) facilitates the association with social groups and subcultures involved with more dangerous drugs, such as opiates or barbiturates. Transition to the use of such drugs would be a consequence of this association rather than an inherent effect of cannabis. The harm to society derived from abuse of cannabis rests in the economic consequences of the impairment of the individual's social functions and his enhanced proneness to asocial and antisocial behavior.''

Mescaline, Psilocybin, DMT

For centuries, various Indian tribes have used mescaline (derived from the Mexican cactus, peyote) in religious ceremonies. Mescaline is available on the illicit market as a crystalline powder in capsules or as a liquid in ampuls or vials. It may also be obtained as whole cactus "buttons," chopped "buttons" in capsules, or as a brownish-gray cloudy liquid. The drug is generally taken orally, but may be injected. Because of its bitter taste, the drug is often ingested with tea, coffee, milk, orange juice or some other common beverage.

Psilocybin is derived from certain mushrooms found in Mexico. It has been used in Indian religious rites as far back as pre-Columbian times. It is not nearly as potent as LSD, but with adequate doses, similar hallucinogenic effects are produced. Psilocybin is available in crystalline, powdered or liquid form.

DMT (dimethyltryptamine) is a more recent addition to the list of presently abused hallucinogenic agents. Although prepared synthetically, it is a natural constituent of the seeds of certain plants found in the West Indies and South America. Powder made from these seeds is known to have been used as a snuff as far back as the arrival of Columbus in the New World—and is still used by some Indian tribes of South America. DMT produces effects similar to those of LSD, but much larger doses are required.

Some varieties of morning glory seeds are also abused for their hallucinogenic effects. The bizarre behavioral effects produced upon ingestion are probably attributable to LSD-like components.

LSD

LSD (lysergic acid diethylamide) was synthesized in 1938 from lysergic acid present in ergot, a fungus that grows on rye. LSD is the most potent of the hallucinogens. On the illicit market, the drug may be obtained as a small white pill, as a crystalline powder in capsules, or as a tasteless, colorless or odorless liquid in ampuls.

Frequently, it is offered in the form of impregnated sugar cubes, cookies or crackers. LSD is usually taken orally, but may be injected.

LSD primarily affects the central nervous system, producing changes in mood and behavior. The user may also exhibit dilated pupils, tremor, elevated temperature and blood pressure, and hyperactive reflexes. Tolerance to the behavioral effects of LSD may develop with several days of continued use, but physical dependence does not occur. Although psychic dependence may develop, it is seldom intense. Accordingly, most LSD devotees will use the drug when available, but do not seem to experience a serious craving when LSD cannot be obtained.

In general, the LSD experience consists of changes in perception, thought, mood and activity. Perceptual changes involve senses of sight, hearing, touch, body image and time. Colors seem to intensify or change, shape and spatial relation appear distorted, objects seem to pulsate, two-dimensional objects appear to become three dimensional and inanimate objects seem to assume emotional import. Sensitivity to sound increases but the source of the sound is elusive. Conversations can be heard but may not be compre-hended. There may be auditory hallucinations of music and voices. There may be changes in taste and food may feel gritty. Cloth seems to change texture, becoming coarse and dry or fine and velvety. The subject may feel cold or sweaty. There are sensations of light-headedness, emptiness, shaking, vibrations, fogginess. Subjects lose awareness of their bodies with a resultant floating feeling. Arms or legs may be held in one position for extended periods of time. Time seems to race, stop, slow down or even go backwards. Changes in thought include a free flow of bizarre ideas including notions of persecution. Trivial events assume unusual significance and im-portance. An inspiration or insight phenomenon is claimed by some LSD adherents.

The mood effects of LSD run the gamut. There may be bursts of tears, of laughter, or the subject may feel no emotion at all. A state of complete relaxation and happiness, not apparent to an observer, may be experienced. A feeling of being alone and cut off from the world may lead to anxiety, fear and panic. Accordingly, the LSD session is frequently monitored by an abstaining LSD-experienced friend to prevent flight, suicidal attempts, dangerous reaction to panic states, and impulsive behavior, such as disrobing.

There may be a feeling of enhanced creativity, but this subjective feeling rarely seems to produce objective results.

After a number of hours, the effects of LSD begin to wear off. Waves of the LSD experience, diminishing in intensity, alternate with periods of no effects at all, until all symptoms disappear. Some fatigue, tension, and recurrent hallucinations may persist long after ingestion of the drug. Psychological changes induced by the drug can persist for indefinite periods.

There is, at present, no approved general medical use for LSD. Some interesting results have been obtained with the drug in certain medically supervised research programs—particularly in the treatment of chronic alcoholism and terminal illness. However, the Food and Drug Administration now takes the position that LSD has insufficient clinical utility to warrant either prescription or nonprescription use. Consequently, LSD is now subject to controls similar to those for any unproven investigational drug.

Medical warnings notwithstanding, large quantities of the drug have become available on an illicit basis for use in "mind expansion" —an application not even contemplated in medical research programs undertaken to date. Those using LSD for this purpose advocate unrestricted use of the product. They state that the drug is not inherently dangerous, claiming either personal use without complication or citing safe use by various notables from many fields. Although it may be true that some individuals have had LSD experiences without apparent ill effect, growing medical evidence shows the drug can cause very serious, and often damaging reactions in many. Hospital admissions of persons with acute LSD-induced psychoses are on the increase. Bizarre behavior in public, panic, fear, and homicidal and suicidal urges have been reported. Psychotic states have been induced through use of the drug—both with emotionally unstable individuals and with persons in whom no sign of emotional instability had been evident. Although most LSD-induced psychotic episodes have occurred in persons initially experimenting with the drug, untoward results have also occurred with "experienced" abusers. What's more, "casualties" have happened even when the drug has been taken under supervision, both medical and nonmedical. LSD also can produce delayed psychotic reactions in some individuals. In some instances, hallucinations have recurred for weeks after the drug was taken. In the opinion of Dr.

James L. Goddard, Commissioner of Food and Drugs, medically un-
supervised use of LSD is analogous to playing "chemical Russian
roulette."

SOLVENTS

Among non-drug substances frequently encountered in drug abuse
situations are various solvents. For example, the inhalation of
solvent fumes from glue, gasoline, paint thinner and lighter fluid
will produce a form of intoxication. Inhalation is practiced most
frequently by youngsters between 10 and 15 and occasionally up
to 18 years. Glue usually is squeezed into a handkerchief or bag
which is placed over the nose and mouth. Gasoline and paint
thinner fumes may be inhaled directly from tanks and cans.

After a number of "drags," the individual experiences excitation,
exhilaration and excitement resembling the initial effects of alcoholic intoxication. Blurring of vision, ringing ears, slurred speech
and staggering are common, as are hallucinations. This phase of
intoxication lasts from 30-45 minutes after inhalation, followed by
drowsiness, stupor and even unconsciousness of about an hour's
duration. Upon recovery, the individual usually does not recall
what happened during the period of intoxication.

Present knowledge concerning solvent inhalation indicates that
physical dependence does not develop with the abuse of these
agents, although a tendency to increase the amount inhaled sug-
gests tolerance. Repeated use and relapse to use indicate the
development of psychic dependence.

Some medical problems can attend solvent inhalation. The chief
dangers of inhaling these substances are death by suffocation, the
development of psychotic behavior, and the state of intoxication
these substances produce. Additionally, a severe type of anemia
has been observed in glue-sniffers who have an inherited defect of
the blood cells (sickle-cell disease). It is known that many solvents
and the ingredients of some types of glue can damage the kidneys,
liver, heart, blood and nervous system. Although such adverse
effects as a result of *inhalation* have not been established, they remain a distinct possibility.

PART III:
THE DRUG ABUSER
AND METHODS
OF THERAPY

Although much is known about the effects of drugs with abuse potential, the abuser himself remains an enigma. Slum conditions, easy access to drugs, peddlers and organized crime have all been blamed for the problem. But while any of these factors may contribute, no single cause nor single set of conditions clearly leads to drug dependency—for it occurs in all social and economic classes. The key to the riddle lies within the abuser himself. True, drug dependency cannot develop without a chemical agent. Yet, while millions are exposed to drugs by reason of medical need, relatively few turn to a life of drugs. Even in metropolitan areas, where drugs may be available on street corners, only a small percentage of the individuals exposed join the ranks of the abusers.

For the most part, the hard-core abuser suffers from certain types of emotional instability which may or may not have been apparent prior to his initial drug abuse experience. Occasional cases may have a background (often undiagnosed) of psychiatric disorder.

Some psychiatrists have said that addicts have an inherent inability to develop meaningful interpersonal relationships. Others have said that addicts are persons who are unwilling to face the responsibility of maturity. Adolescent addicts may have suffered childhood deprivation or overprotectiveness. Or, they simply may not be able to cope with the physical and emotional changes accompanying this period. It is significant that many addicts have their first drug experience in their teens.

The transition from childhood to adulthood is seldom smooth, and many individuals are not emotionally equipped to meet the demands they face. The early and middle teens bring a loosening of family ties, a diminution of parental authority, increasing responsibility and sexual maturing. Beset with anxiety, frustration, fear of failure, inner conflicts and doubts, the adolescent may find that amphetamine and marihuana promote conversation and friendship, barbiturates loosen inhibitions, hallucinogens heighten sensations and narcotics provide relief and escape. Drug abuse may provide the entrée to an "in group" or be a way of affirming independence by defying authority and convention.

In general, drug abusers fall into three main groups. The first group employs drugs for a specific or "situational" purpose. Examples: the student who uses amphetamine to keep awake at exam time; the housewife who uses anti-obesity pills for additional energy to get through household chores; the salesman who uses amphetamine to keep awake while driving all night to an early morning appointment. Such individuals may or may not exhibit psychological and/or physical dependence.

The second group consists of "spree" users, usually of college or high school age. Drugs are used for "kicks," or just the experience. There may be some degree of psychological dependence, but little or no physical dependence because of the sporadic and mixed pattern of use. Drug sprees constitute a defiance of convention, an adventurous, daring experience, or a means of having fun. Unlike hard-core abusers, who often pursue their habit alone or in pairs, spree users usually take drugs only in group or social situations.

The third is the "hard-core" addict. His activities revolve almost entirely around drug experiences and securing supplies. He exhibits strong psychological dependence on the drug, often reinforced by physical dependence when certain drugs are being used. Typically, the hard-core addict began drug abuse on a spree basis. He has been on drugs for some time and presently feels that he cannot function without drug support.

Obviously, there is much overlapping between these groups, and a "spree" user or "situational" user may deteriorate to the "hard-core" group. The transition occurs when the interaction between drug effects and personality causes a loss of control over drug use. The drug becomes a means of solving or avoiding life's problems.

Slum sections of large metropolitan areas still account for the largest number of *known* drug abusers. But frustration, immaturity, and emotional deprivation are not peculiar to depressed neighborhoods, and the misuse of drugs by middle and upper economic class individuals is being recognized with increasing frequency. Drug dependency is not discriminating. A drug, an individual, an environment which predisposes use, and a personality deficiency are the key factors in its development.

Therapy—General Considerations

Until recently, the public has regarded addicts as incurable. Once "hooked," there was no road back. This idea arose from the fact that so many opiate addicts relapsed to drug use, even after long periods of hospitalization. Not long ago, treatment for addiction consisted of little more than detoxification (drug withdrawal). When more ambitious programs were attempted, they had only limited success in terms of number of "cures"—but each contributed to a growing body of knowledge about the addict, the drugs he uses, and ways to effect his rehabilitation.

Today, there is general agreement that, to be successful, a treatment program should include, not only controlled detoxification, but also psychiatric evaluation and therapy, and continued medical supervision and counseling upon return to the community. While reduced drug dependency is one goal, the prime objective is total abstinence from drugs.

Initial detoxification of severely addicted persons is most safely accomplished under medical supervision in a hospital setting. There, the patient's drug intake can be limited to physician-prescribed medications, including drugs administered for purposes of gradual, controlled withdrawal. In addition, examinations can be conducted to discern if there are underlying mental and emotional disorders. If disorders are diagnosed, psychiatric consultation, group therapy and other treatment can be arranged as needed.

After detoxification, and after he has demonstrated ability to cope with stress situations in a protected environment, the former addict can be returned to the community. This is the most critical period in the abuser's rehabilitation. He is still not emotionally equipped to face, without special help, many situations and problems presented by the outside world. For example, neither the neighborhood in which he was introduced to drugs, nor his drug-using friends, have changed during his absence. Accordingly, the pressures to use drugs again will be enormous. To help him resist these pressures, trained personnel, working with community organizations, should be assigned to provide guidance and support during times of crisis. Initially, he might be required to maintain contact with a caseworker, keep psychiatric or other medical appointments and attend group therapy sessions. The degree and duration of such supervision would depend on the rate of rehabilitation. Conceivably, several years might elapse before a former addict could be discharged as "cured."

Aside from helping "ex-addicts" rehabilitate themselves, community health organizations can provide an opportunity for *initial* contact between the active drug abuser and those who can help him. Addicts frequently experience a desire to "get off drugs," particularly when their supply of drugs or money is running low. This desire may be short-lived, but at such times, addicts may present themselves at clinics and request help. Although addicts may be poorly motivated when they step in the door, properly trained counselors can sometimes persuade them to enter treatment programs.

Such programs must be flexible and subject to modification in accordance with the needs of the individual abuser. For example, a "spree user" who has developed neither physical dependence nor psychological dependence will rarely, if ever, require hospitalization. He may, however, need psychiatric evaluation to determine whether he has any underlying emotional or mental disorders requiring medical attention. In some cases, only counseling services will be indicated. The "hard-core" abuser, on the other hand, will seldom achieve complete abstinence from drugs unless he commits himself to the complete program. But even this degree of commit-

48

ment may not prevent relapses. Return to drug use (recidivism) is not uncommon—even after relatively long "clean" periods.

As is true of alcohol abuse, it is generally recognized that relapse, in itself, is not a sign of complete failure or incurability. The ingrained habits and response patterns of years aren't changed in a few weeks or months. The way back to a useful independent place in society is long and hard for the addict. But as knowledge about drug addiction and its causes accumulates, the chances for rehabilitation will be increased.

At present, most facilities for the treatment and rehabilitation of the drug abuser do not begin to meet the requirements outlined above. Addicts are difficult patients at best, and many hospitals will not knowingly accept them for detoxification, let alone treatment. Community health centers, generally too few and far between, are almost never equipped to provide the close supervision and long-term follow-up essential to a drug addict's rehabilitation. By and large, the few clinics which do operate solely to help addicts are ill-equipped and understaffed. Moreover, they are frequently ignored by neighboring community and professional organizations whose cooperation is needed to provide medical care and employment opportunities.

New Approaches

The situation, however, is far from static. On the Federal level, recognition that addicts are sick people led to enactment of the Narcotic Addict Rehabilitation Act in November, 1966. The act provides for civil commitment of addicts—those charged with violating Federal criminal laws as well as those not facing such charges—for the purpose of treatment and rehabilitation. The act further provides for aftercare within the addicts' own communities. Other evidence of Federal concern: Since January, 1967, the Federal hospital at Lexington, Kentucky, has been designated a drug abuse research institution under a program administered by the National Institute of Mental Health. (NIMH also has taken over the Fort Worth facility where other special programs are contemplated.)

During the 1960's, many new kinds of treatment programs have been initiated in various states and municipalities—both on the governmental and nongovernmental level. Most such programs are still considered experimental. Some of the better known programs (all of which have provoked varying degrees of controversy) are as follows:

Maryland Program. In Maryland, a special outpatient clinic has been established by the state for addict-parolees from correctional institutions. The addict-parolee must report every evening to leave a urine specimen (to test for the presence of narcotics), must attend group psychotherapy at the clinic once a week and must maintain a job. Failure to comply with these requirements can lead to immediate return to prison.

California Program. In 1961, the California legislature provided for a program of civil commitment in which addicts are sent to a rehabilitation center for group psychotherapy, remedial education, vocational training, and counseling for patients and their families. A condition of participation in the program is that, following release as outpatients, addicts must submit to periodic tests utilizing 'Nalline' (nalorphine hydrochloride, Merck Sharp & Dohme). 'Nalline' is a synthetic *anti-narcotic* which brings about abrupt withdrawal symptoms if a person is using narcotics. Since 1965, the program has also provided halfway houses where outpatients who feel unable to adjust immediately to community life may stay as long as 90 days.

Narcotics Anonymous. Narcotics Anonymous, modeled after Alcoholics Anonymous, has chapters in major cities. Spiritually oriented, it relies on mutual inspiration, discussion and the therapeutic value of confession. As with AA, ex-addicts in the program can contact fellow members at any time they need to talk about personal problems and pressures.

Synanon. One of the most controversial nongovernmental projects is Synanon, a group of residences throughout the country managed by ex-addicts. Because of rigid requirements for entry into the group, usually only those individuals highly motivated to abandon drug abuse are candidates for admission. Once in, the ex-addict is assigned tasks and encouraged to work toward greater responsibility within the organization. To date, most Synanon "graduates" have remained in the Synanon community.

Daytop Lodge. In 1963, under a grant by the National Institute of Mental Health, Daytop Lodge was opened on Staten Island, New

York, for the treatment of addict probationers. Directed by Synanon graduates, the Lodge is a residential facility designed to ease the ex-addict's transition into community life. The program utilizes small group sessions in which participants air their emotional problems.

Methadone Program. Another highly controversial experiment is the methadone program initiated by the Rockefeller Institute. The program is in operation in New York City. Former heroin addicts with a history of recidivism are stabilized on methadone—a long-acting synthetic narcotic. The drug is reputed to relieve narcotic hunger without producing euphoric-like effects. It is also claimed that methadone blocks the euphoric-like impressions of heroin. The program, for patients 19-37 years of age, provides maintenance doses of methadone for as long as necessary. The drug is administered in the presence of a clinic nurse. The program aims at making the patient a basically normal, self-reliant individual through classes leading to a high school equivalency certificate, and through job placement.

The "British System"

In discussions of what should be done about the addict and his need for drugs, frequent mention is made of the "British System" for treating addiction. In actuality more of an approach than a system, it stems from an attitude shared by government, law enforcement authorities, the medical profession and the general public that drug addiction is a disease, not a crime. Consequently, physicians, at their discretion, may prescribe narcotics for addicts if complete withdrawal would be hazardous to the patient's health, or if the patient would be incapable of leading a useful, normal life without maintenance doses. However, the physician is not expected to resort to maintenance doses until every effort has been made to effect a cure.

To obtain treatment, an addict must present himself to a doctor and discuss his problem. If the physician accepts the patient (he is not obliged to do so), he is obligated to attempt a cure. Failing this, he is expected to attempt to convince his patient to enter an institution for drug withdrawal. Only after these measures fail, and following review of the case by other experts, may the physician prescribe maintenance doses ("nonprogressive amounts, usually small"). The physician is expected to keep drug supplies within limits of what is medically necessary, which means he must maintain continual observation of the patient's condition.

To insure that addicts are limiting narcotic acquisitions to their medically determined needs, police regularly inspect pharmacy records. Under the Dangerous Drug Act of 1920, pharmacists must keep records of all transactions involving the controlled drugs.

Direct police action concerns itself only with illegal drug traffic and law-breaking addicts. Addicts can be prosecuted for forging prescriptions, going to more than one doctor at a time in order to get duplicate narcotic prescriptions, or obtaining drugs illegally. Physicians suspected of overprescribing are reported to the Dangerous Drug Branch of the Home Office.

The present approach to treating addiction, established in 1926, is the result of a special report defining the relationship of doctors and their addict-patients. For years this approach operated smoothly—due to a number of factors: among them, the virtual lack of a black market in heroin and cocaine, and a small known addict population. In 1959, the addict population was reported at 454—out of a population of 50 million.

The "British System," however, has not been foolproof, according to the 1965 Report of the Interdepartmental Committee on Drug Addiction (second Brain Committee Report). The Committee reported "a disturbing rise in the incidence of addiction to heroin and cocaine, especially among young people." Concern was expressed, too, over "wider consumption" of stimulant drugs by youth. The Committee also found that a few physicians were prescribing excessive quantities of addictive drugs, leading to the inference that "known" addicts were supplying others who had no reference to physicians for addiction treatment.

Because of this increase in drug abuse—straining the control capabilities of individual physicians and hospital facilities—the Report recommended that special centers be established for addiction treatment. Under this proposal, the prescribing of heroin and cocaine for addicts would be restricted to physicians on the staffs of such centers. It has also been suggested that the centers be given the power to detain addicts who seek discharge before treatment has been completed. It is interesting to note that, in an earlier report of the same Interdepartmental Committee, *only* institutional treatment was found likely to be satisfactory in the treatment of addiction.

Although the recent proposals reflect no fundamental change in the British attitude toward drug dependence, they suggest that failure to provide stricter control of prescribing, as well as additional facilities for treatment, will lead to a large-scale black market in narcotics. This, in turn, would require more stringent law enforcement—a pattern not unlike that which prevails, at present, in the United States.

PART IV:
EDUCATIONAL
APPROACHES

The educational objective of a drug abuse program is the same whatever the level of instruction—elementary, secondary school, or college: to *prevent* the development of an actual drug abuse situation.

To achieve this objective, it is imperative that the educator present his students with accurate information on the drugs in question. The importance of this is indicated by drug abusers themselves. Almost without exception, these people state that prior information about drug abuse might have prevented their involvement— particularly where curiosity or thrill-seeking was the apparent motivating factor in their introduction to drugs.

Educators should also avoid preaching or moralizing, another point on which addicts seem to be in general agreement. They state that such an approach can push a youngster toward drug experimenta- tion—rather than make him give up the idea. One addict put it this way: "When I first started using junk (drugs), I did it because I wasn't supposed to. In those days, anything I was told not to do was what I did. In my crowd, that's how you proved you were a man."

Obviously, the factors that lead to drug abuse are many and complex, and no simple explanation or clear-cut course of action will fit every situation. Flexibility in dealing with the problem may, therefore, be the key to successfully explaining it—despite the fact that certain individuals will continue to be susceptible to drug abuse no matter what is done short of intensive psychiatric care. But many youngsters can be dissuaded from drug experimentation if they are approached on the subject in a forthright way—an approach which will enable them to grasp the implications of abuse and so make sound decisions.

What follows reflects the philosophy that prevention, based on an objective presentation of all applicable facts, is the key to minimizing the possibility of drug abuse by young people.

ELEMENTARY SCHOOL LEVEL

The elementary grades offer the first opportunity to present formal instruction concerning the principles of good health practices. The subject of drugs: what they are, what their benefits are and how they should be used, is not too complex for young minds.

In the early grades, the teacher should strive to develop an awareness that drugs and household chemicals have proper uses, but that their potentially dangerous nature demands the youngster's respect. Discussions of drug abuse should be concerned with the dangers of taking things from medicine chests, closets, etc., without parental permission; accepting what appears to be candy from strangers; and the sniffing of fumes from glue, paint, gasoline, cleaning fluid and other volatile substances around the home. Children should be encouraged to report to their parents or teachers any strange feelings of dizziness or illness following the ingestion of *any* substance, including foods and drugs.

Sniffing glue and other volatile substances may be attempted "for kicks" by children as early as ten years of age. Often, an older brother or sister will introduce them to the practice. Therefore, discussions of this form of abuse might be introduced as early as the fifth or sixth grades for purposes of prevention—particularly in areas where drug abuse is endemic. If information is presented in a simple, forthright manner, a child of ten or eleven years will begin to understand the effects, dangers and causes of inhaling the fumes of chemicals. The teacher may find that pupils know about other types of abuse (e.g., abuse of "pills" and narcotics) and should be prepared to answer questions accordingly.

Teaching the Subject

On the elementary level, the subject of drugs is best presented as a part of health instruction. If children come from neighborhoods where drug abuse is a serious problem, the teacher may find them more sophisticated on the subject than many adults. But whatever the level of sophistication, the teacher's job is to keep pupils from becoming personally involved with drugs. Consequently, the teacher must be prepared to give them as much information as they can absorb and should freely discuss how to avoid becoming involved. The teacher should encourage students to ask questions on the subject, and be prepared with *factual* answers. In many areas, particularly those which are economically deprived, it is well to understand that use of drugs among young people is often considered a sign of maturity, of being "in." The teacher's goal is to demonstrate, without preaching, that drug abuse is not smart— that the "pleasures" drugs may provide are transitory at best— while the dangers inherent in their use can damage one for a lifetime.

In communities where drug abuse is not widespread, the tendency is to believe that "nice kids" don't abuse drugs. The truth is that "nice kids" are often as fascinated by drugs as are the underprivileged. The motivation may differ—"kicks" rather than peer-group reputation may be involved—but the problem knows no socioeconomic boundaries, and emotional deprivation, an underlying cause for drug abuse, can occur in any family. Here again, the prime requisite in approaching the problem is candor. Scare techniques and preaching should be avoided. Facts, well presented, should have impact enough—particularly as knowledge concerning the problem is usually less widespread among these children. Most youngsters appreciate frank talk which reveals, in a matter-of-fact way, what the dangers are—and that it is a sign of maturity to reject drugs rather than use them.

Suggested Discussion Topics

- Health and sickness: What keeps us healthy, what makes us sick?
- Use of medicines for prevention and cure of sickness.
- Dangers of improperly used medicines.
- Hazards posed by abuse of nonmedical substances such as glue, gasoline, etc.
- Manner in which boys and girls are introduced to drug abuse.
- Handling situations in which drugs or other abusable substances are offered.
- The importance of not "going along with the crowd" or "taking a dare."
- Effects of drug abuse on general health and social behavior.
- Relationship between drug abuse and juvenile delinquency and crime.
- Impact of addiction on one's future.
- How students can assist in solving drug abuse problems.

Other Activities

- Have students collect newspaper and magazine articles dealing with accidental poisonings, safe use of household products and medicines. Have them make scrapbooks or arrange articles as a bulletin board exhibit.
- Dramatize a situation in which a student is urged by his friends to take a dare and ingest an unknown substance.
- Have students make posters warning about drug abuse.
- Have students write essays on the value of medicines properly used—and the dangers of drugs improperly used.
- Install a question box in which students might submit problems for discussion.

Topics for Study

Depending on the grade level, one or more of these topics may be suitable for special projects in the form of booklets, including graphs and pictures, or as oral reports. Classes may be divided into committees.

- The story of drugs in medicine.
- Narcotics in medical use.
- The effect of narcotic and non-narcotic drug abuse on the body.
- What local community agencies do to cope with drug abuse and addiction.

SECONDARY SCHOOL LEVEL

Many secondary school pupils already have considerable information—and misinformation—about drugs. In the main, this has been gleaned from motion pictures, magazines and newspaper accounts. But much of what they "know" has come from friends—some of whom may have even experimented with drugs.

Teen-agers' lack of understanding of the dangers of drug abuse makes it imperative that they be apprised of what the effects of abusing drugs can be. Equally important, they must realize that drug abuse can lead to incidents that will result in delinquency records that can mitigate against employment in many places, and entrance to almost any college.

Reaching teen-agers on this subject is not easy, due, in part, to the vast amount of misinformation that has come their way. But they can be reached if the instruction is sufficiently comprehensive, and if preaching is avoided in favor of a presentation that will encourage them to make a wise *choice* should they one day face the pressure of "going along with the crowd."

Teaching the Subject

The manner in which the subject of drug abuse is presented will depend on the maturity and personalities of the students. Background lectures, films and pupil presentations may be used. But whatever the approach, ample time for class discussion should be provided. Drug abuse is a controversial subject and misinformation is widespread. All sides of the issue should be aired, so that students can draw their own conclusions. In these discussions, a good technique is to encourage an exchange of ideas between students—with the teacher acting mainly as moderator or information authority when clarification of facts is needed. If the group is reasonably mature, it might best be handled according to techniques suggested for college students (see page 61 of this section). In any case, the instructor should be familiar with the subjects listed below—and may wish to touch on them in preliminary discussions. Ideally, instruction on drug abuse should be part of a planned, sequential health curriculum that affords teaching opportunities in health education classes, the social sciences, physiology, etc. Coordination of effort in these areas will ensure maximal student impact.

Suggested Discussion Topics

- History of narcotics in medicine and as drugs of abuse.
- Use and abuse of non-narcotics.
- Dangers of self-medication, stressing use of barbiturates and amphetamine.
- Drug abuse problems in the United States and other countries.
- Drug addiction and the drug addict. Different types of drug abusers.
- Legislation, national and international, to control manufacture, sale, and distribution of narcotics and other habit-forming drugs.
- Legal and illegal distribution of drugs.
- Effects of narcotics and other abusable drugs on personal health and behavior.
- Ways in which persons are introduced to abuse drugs: at parties, through friends, by the group, etc.
- Dealing with situations in which habit-forming drugs are offered.
- Current approaches to treatment of addiction.
- Relationship between drug abuse, juvenile delinquency and crime.
- Attitude of society toward drug abusers.
- Effects on one's future from being associated with drug abuse.
- How students can assist in the problem of drug abuse.

Suggested Activities

- Have students collect newspaper items, magazine articles and authoritative pamphlets on drug abuse for class discussion and development of a class resource file.
- Have students compile list of community agencies concerned with drug abuse. What are their roles and responsibilities? (Field trips should be arranged—if feasible.)
- Set up classroom student panel to discuss drug abuse. Encourage students to do the same for community or PTA meetings.
- Have students role-play a situation in which a student is approached to try narcotics. How should he react?
- Have students prepare charts, graphs and an historical chronology of drug abuse since 1900.
- Invite persons with professional experience on drug abuse problems to participate in class activities. If possible, through official sources, invite someone who has been an addict or has abused drugs.

- Have students prepare essays or short stories on drug abuse themes. Outstanding articles might be considered for school newspaper.
- Have students send away for literature on drug addiction issued by the World Health Organization (UN), Federal Bureau of Narcotics, Bureau of Drug Abuse Control (FDA), U.S. Public Health Service, American Medical Association, local police department and other agencies.
- Have students prepare research papers on such topics as the status and nature of drug abuse in the United States, effects of narcotics on general health, and techniques for treating addiction.

COLLEGE LEVEL

The college situation invites experimentation in many aspects of life—and drug experimentation is no exception. Accordingly, in-depth instruction on drug abuse problems should be given to every student early in his college career. Logical areas to handle such instruction might include health education, sociology, and psychology. Guidance counselors also may have opportunities to educate students on the subject.

In considering the problem of effectively reaching people of college age, the instructor faces a dilemma: If he "preaches," if he resorts to a recitation of "thou shalt not," he will lose them. On the other hand, he must make clear that *any* involvement with drug abuse, should it become known publicly, can adversely affect the future of the person concerned. For example, records which indicate someone has been *suspected* of drug abuse could mitigate against future employment by most government agencies (and such agencies often conduct background investigations of prospective employees). Any reason to believe that an individual has been involved, directly or indirectly, in drug abuse, can become an important factor in one's acceptance or rejection by medical schools, law schools and other graduate schools. And it does no good to philosophize about the justice or injustice of this: it's the way things are . . . and what may be at stake when one becomes involved in a drug abuse situation . . . even without being an active participant. In short, there are dangers in drug abuse that are neither physiological nor psychological . . . and students must be aware of them. The time and place to raise these points will depend on the way discussion of the general problem proceeds. But the points must be made—in addition, of course, to the no less important medical reasons for abstaining from drug abuse.

Marihuana

At present, the most popular illicit abuse drug encountered on the campus is marihuana. It is also the drug about which most misinformation exists.

Some of the confusion regarding marihuana may stem from the fact that, while not a narcotic, it is controlled by the Federal Bureau of Narcotics. This classification has given rise to reports that the effects of this drug are as damaging—and can be as addictive—as those of heroin. College-age youth know this isn't so . . . and recognition of the fact by the instructor early in any discussion will help greatly in winning the confidence of the group.

Students invariably will ask whether it isn't true that the effects of marihuana are less dangerous than the effects of alcohol. There is no universal agreement among experts who have studied this question. Some say "yes" . . . some say "no." But almost without exception, these persons agree that marihuana is a *dangerous* drug. Two such authorities, both of whom, incidentally, advocate reform (but not elimination) of current restrictive marihuana legislation, have commented on the subject as follows: Speaking before some 2000 college students late last year, Donald Louria, M.D., Chairman of the New York State Council on Drug Addiction and a professor at Cornell University Medical College, said, ". . . we must not overreact to (marihuana's) . . . use (but) . . . we cannot afford to legalize it." Similar sentiments have been expressed by Lawrence Kolb, M.D., Assistant Surgeon General (retired) of the U.S. Public Health Service. Says Dr. Kolb: "Marihuana is undoubtedly a . . . harmful drug."

Still, the question may be raised that, if marihuana can be less dangerous than alcohol, why is it so stringently controlled? Again citing Dr. Kolb: "Alcohol, during the past 2500 years, has apparently become an irreplaceable part of our social structure. We know that it does much harm, but the fact that we tolerate this harm is no reason for permitting the indiscriminate use of another intoxicant."

What kind of student will be attracted to marihuana use . . . and what motivates this behavior? In considering these questions, it is well to realize that students who use the drug may come from any kind of background . . . and that emotional instability is not a prerequisite to marihuana curiosity. In the public mind, the type of student who may be expected to use marihuana is the one whose dress, deportment and interests are farthest from those traditionally associated with campus life. Although marihuana use by individuals who make much of nonconformity is not unusual, the drug is occasionally used by those for whom nonconformity holds no special appeal. However, the more conservative type of student is less likely to join demonstrations in favor of uncontrolled drug use; nor is he likely to flaunt his interest in marihuana as a badge of personal freedom.

Although no conclusive studies on the subject are available, persons who have been close to the problem have suggested that the motivations for using marihuana are many and sometimes complex. To be sure, there is use simply "for kicks." But for some individuals, mainly occasional users, marihuana use may also be symbolic of their separation from parental or other authoritarian control.

Frequently, the appeal is that which always attends what is forbidden. And, for many, use is the key to belonging to a special group. (Interestingly enough, there are some reports that marihuana cliques are often less interested in alcoholic consumption than are "normal" college groups.) For those who are emotionally unstable, the drug may seem to provide whatever it takes to cope with one's problems—be they temporary or deep-rooted.

Other Drugs

Although LSD use appears to be increasing on college campuses, the scope of the problem does not, at this time, approach that of marihuana use. But the considerations that apply to this new and vastly more potent hallucinogen are essentially the same as those for marihuana—except that there is considerable evidence that the psychological damage potential of LSD is very great. Suicidal or homicidal tendencies have been reported. Even Dr. Timothy Leary, a leading advocate of LSD use, recognizes these dangers and speaks, with concern, about "LSD casualties."

Chronic abuse of amphetamine and barbiturates presently attracts relatively few people on the college campus—but these drugs are abused widely on an occasional or spree basis. Not infrequently, this occurs under special stress situations such as those encountered at exam time. (They are not generally regarded as "kick" or "in" drugs on the campus.) Because little social opprobrium is attached to such drugs, it is difficult to combat their abuse. However, rational discussion, based on accurate knowledge of the potentially damaging effects of these drugs, may dissuade many from their abuse.

Because of the great publicity that has attended heroin use, most college students, mindful of the dangers involved, abjure this drug. But the fact is that heroin addicts have almost all, at one time, used less dangerous drugs of abuse such as marihuana. At this point, medical experts are in general agreement that heroin users usually are individuals with severe emotional disorders. It is also widely thought that misuse of nonaddictive drugs by such persons can trigger heroin use by overcoming the usual drug abuse restraints.

Discussion Setting

In preparing for general discussion of drug abuse, it is well to realize that some students may already have experimented with nonaddictive drugs such as amphetamine or hallucinogens. Having firsthand knowledge of the effects of these drugs, based on personal (though often limited) experiences, they may be skeptical of information citing physiological or psychological dangers. When such students express their views, the instructor should never be reluctant to agree with what is factual and to admit lack of knowledge in those areas where scientific data are still incomplete. But he will serve all students if he can convince them that enough questions remain unanswered to warrant abstention from possibly dangerous experimentation. To reinforce this contention, the instructor should become familiar with the history and pharmacology of drugs of abuse; characteristics of different types of abusers (hard-core, occasional, etc.); causative factors (sociological, psychological, pharmacologic); patterns of distribution of legal and illegal drugs; legislation and enforcement; and problems of rehabilitation.

When the subject is drug abuse, the instructional situation can greatly affect the results obtained. Ideally, it should provide students with opportunities to express opinions, cite experiences and challenge others. From the standpoint of student participation, seminars, symposia or panel discussions—sponsored by one or more departments, or by student activities groups—would be preferable to formalized lectures. An informal discussion group in a fraternity house, dormitory or student union building might also prove useful.

But whatever the setting, the goal of the instructor should be to stimulate critical thinking on the subject. Consequently, he should act principally as a moderator—and as an arbiter to resolve questions of fact which may be at issue.

PART V: PROBLEMS OF ABUSER IDENTIFICATION

Instructors, traditionally concerned with the general health of students and alert to departures from "normal" for any individuals, will find it extremely difficult to recognize drug abusers. Although drug abuse in its various forms can produce identifiable effects, almost all such manifestations are, at their onset, identical to those produced by conditions having nothing whatever to do with drug abuse. What's more, some students may be using legitimate drugs in accordance with physicians' instructions—but without their teachers' knowledge. For example, such disorders as epilepsy, diabetes or asthma may require maintenance drug therapy that will produce low-level side effects. Or, a student might be drowsy from ingesting a nonprescription product—such as an antihistamine. Whatever the reason, a student appearing unwell or disturbed will be cause for concern on the part of an educator. But a clue to the possibility of drug abuse comes with persistence of symptoms which might otherwise appear "routine."

Although it is difficult to recognize drug abusers, many *potential* "hard-core" addicts can be rehabilitated if their involvement in drug abuse is spotted in its early stages . . . when professional help can be brought to bear on the problem in an effective manner. Instructors, therefore, in addition to their educational role, are properly concerned with identification of abusers—wherever and whenever circumstances indicate this possibility.

Common Symptoms of Drug Abuse

Not all drug abuse-related character changes appear detrimental, at least in the initial stages. For example, a usually bored, sleepy student may—while using amphetamine—be more alert and thereby improve performance. A nervous, high-strung individual may, on barbiturates, be more cooperative and easier to manage.

What teachers must look for, consequently, are not simply changes for the worse, but any sudden changes in behavior out of character with a student's previous conduct. When such behavioral expressions become *usual* for an individual, there is a causal factor. That factor may be drug abuse.

Signs which may suggest drug abuse include sudden and dramatic changes in attendance, discipline and academic performance. With the latter, significant changes in legibility, neatness, and caliber of homework may be observed. Drug abusers may also display unusual degrees of activity or inactivity, as well as sudden and irrational flare-ups involving strong emotion or temper. Significant changes for the worse in personal appearance may be cause for concern, for very often a drug abuser becomes indifferent to his appearance and health habits.

There are other, more specific signs which should arouse suspicions, especially if more than one is exhibited by a single student. Among them are furtive behavior regarding actions and possessions (fear of discovery), sunglasses worn at inappropriate times and places (to hide dilated or constricted pupils), and long-sleeve garments worn constantly, even on hot days (to hide needle marks). Of course, association with known drug abusers is a sign of potential trouble.

Because of the expense of supporting a drug habit, the abuser may be observed trying to borrow money from a number of individuals. If this fails, he will not be reluctant to steal items easily converted to cash, such as cameras, radios, jewelry, etc. And if his habit is severe enough, forcing him to use drugs during the school day, he may be found, at odd times, in places such as closets, storage rooms or parked cars.

In addition to these behavioral clues, which are common to most drug abusers, each form of abuse generally has specific manifestations that help identify those engaged in it. They are as follows:

The Glue Sniffer

The glue or solvent sniffer usually retains the odor of the substance he is inhaling on his breath and clothes. Irritation of the mucous membranes in the mouth and nose may result in excessive nasal secretions. Redness and watering of the eyes are commonly observed. The user may appear intoxicated or lack muscular control, and may complain of double vision, ringing in the ears, vivid dreams and even hallucinations. Drowsiness, stupor and unconsciousness may follow excessive use of the substances.

Discovery of plastic or paper bags and rags or handkerchiefs containing dried plastic cement is a telltale sign that glue-sniffing is being practiced.

The Depressant Abuser

The abuser of a depressant drug, such as the barbiturates and certain tranquilizers, exhibits most of the symptoms of alcohol intoxication with one important exception: there is no odor of alcohol on his breath. Students taking depressants may stagger or stumble in classrooms and halls. The depressant abuser frequently falls into a deep sleep in the classroom. In general, the depressant abuser lacks interest in activity, is drowsy, and may appear to be disoriented.

The Stimulant Abuser

The behavior of the abuser of stimulants, such as amphetamine and related drugs, is characterized by excessive activity. The stimulant abuser is irritable, argumentative, appears extremely nervous and has difficulty sitting still in the classroom. In some cases, the pupils of his eyes will be dilated even in a brightly lit place.

Amphetamine has a drying effect on the mucous membranes of the mouth and nose with resultant bad breath that is unidentifiable as to specific odor such as onion, garlic, alcohol, etc. Because of the dryness of mouth, the amphetamine abuser frequently licks his lips to keep them moist. This often results in chapped and reddened lips, which, in severe cases, may be cracked and raw.

Other observable effects: dryness of the mucous membrane in the nose, causing the abuser to rub and scratch his nose vigorously and frequently to relieve the itching sensation, incessant talking about any subject at hand, and, often, chain smoking.

Finally, the student who is abusing stimulant drugs often goes for long periods of time without sleeping or eating and usually cannot resist letting others know about it.

The Narcotic Abuser

Few narcotic abusers are seen in school situations because they usually cannot function within the ordered confines of such institutions. However, some individuals *begin* narcotic abuse while still attending school. Such individuals are likely to be drinking paregoric or cough medicines containing narcotics. The presence of such bottles in wastebaskets or around school grounds is a clue to this form of abuse. The medicinal odor of these preparations is often detectable on the breath.

Other "beginner" narcotic abusers inhale narcotic drugs such as heroin in powder form. Sometimes, traces of this white powder can be seen around the nostrils. Constant inhaling of narcotic drugs makes nostrils red and raw.

For maximal effect, narcotics usually are injected directly into a vein. The most common site of the injections is the inner surface of the arm at the elbow. After repeated injections, scar tissue ("tracks") develops along the course of such veins. Because of the easy identification of these marks, such narcotic abusers usually wear long sleeves at odd times. Females sometimes use makeup to cover marks. Some males get tattooed at injection sites.

The presence of equipment ("works" or "outfit") used in injecting narcotics is another way to spot the narcotic abuser. Since anyone injecting drugs must keep his equipment handy, it may be found on his person or hidden nearby in a locker, washroom or some place where temporary privacy may be found. The characteristic instruments and accessories are a bent spoon or bottle cap, small ball of cotton, syringe or eyedropper, and a hypodermic needle. All are used in the injection process: the spoon or cap holds the narcotic in a little water for heating over a match or lighter, the cotton acts as a filter as the narcotic is drawn through the needle into the syringe or eyedropper.

The small ball of cotton ("satch cotton") is usually kept after use because it retains a small amount of narcotic that can be extracted if the abuser is unable to obtain additional drugs. The bent spoon or bottle cap used to heat the narcotic is easily identifiable because it becomes blackened by the heating process.

A drug abuser deeply under the influence of narcotics is rarely encountered in the classroom. But if he is, he usually appears lethargic, drowsy ("on the nod") or displays symptoms of deep intoxication. Pupils of the eye are often constricted and fail to respond to light.

The Marihuana User

While marihuana is pharmacologically a hallucinogen, its wide-spread use warrants separate discussion. The user of marihuana ("pot") is unlikely to be recognized in the classroom unless he is heavily under the influence at that time. In the early stages of the drug effect, when the drug acts as a stimulant, the user may be very animated and appear almost hysterical. Loud and rapid talking with great bursts of laughter are common at this stage. In the later stages of the drug effect, the user may seem in a stupor or sleepy. During all the stages, the user usually has dilated pupils.

Marihuana smokers may also be identified by their possession of such cigarettes, often called "sticks," "reefers" or "joints." A marihuana cigarette is often rolled in a double thickness of brownish or off-white cigarette paper. Smaller than a regular cigarette, with the paper twisted or tucked in on both ends, the marihuana cigarette often contains seeds and stems and is greener in color than regular tobacco.

Another clue to the presence of "reefers" is the way in which they are often smoked. Typically, such smoking occurs in a group situation. But because of the rapid burning and harshness of the marihuana cigarette, it is generally passed rapidly, after one or two puffs, to another person. The smoke is deeply inhaled and held in the lungs as long as possible. The cigarette is often cupped in the palms of both hands when inhaling to save all the smoke possible. An additional clue to marihuana use is its odor. Similar to that of burnt rope, the odor is readily noticeable on the breath and clothing.

The Hallucinogen Abuser

It is highly unlikely that students who use hallucinogenic drugs (such as LSD) will do so in a school setting. Such drugs are usually used in a group situation under special conditions designed to enhance their effect. Persons under the influence of hallucinogens usually sit or recline quietly in a dream- or trance-like state. However, the effect of such drugs is not always euphoric. On occasion, users become fearful and experience a degree of terror which may cause them to attempt to escape from the group.

Hallucinogenic drugs are usually taken orally. Although sometimes found in tablet or capsule form, they are most commonly seen as liquids. Users usually put drops of the liquid in beverages, on sugar cubes, crackers, or even on small paper wads or cloth.

IDENTIFICATION OF DRUGS

A frequently asked question is: How can I identify "abuse" drugs? How can I tell them from legitimate prescription medicines?

The answer is that no one can effectively identify a drug by sight, taste or smell. For one reason, all the drugs discussed, except for marihuana, can be found in tablet, capsule, powder and liquid form—and in varying colors and shapes. Even marihuana, which is usually smoked, can be found as a candy. Marihuana cookies and marihuana tea also exist.

The only way, therefore, that most drugs can be correctly identified is through a series of complicated laboratory procedures performed by trained technicians. The best a teacher can do is to *suspect* the possibility of abuse when drugs are found under peculiar circumstances or in the possession of someone exhibiting unusual behavior.

WHAT TO DO

The proper handling of drug abuse situations is of vital concern to classroom teachers, guidance and health personnel, and administrators. Educators often ask, "What do we do if a student appears

72

to be abusing drugs?" There is no easy answer to this question, due to the inherent complexity of drug abuse—including the fundamental difficulty of being *certain* that drug abuse even exists. Additionally, educators must be concerned with the roles they play even *after* a suspicion is confirmed. This can involve ongoing counseling with parents, help with the student's rehabilitation, continuing rapport with law enforcement agencies, and a need to determine if more than one student is affected. Although the responsibilities of school personnel in these areas will vary from school to school, and therefore cannot be individually delineated here, everyone concerned with education should be familiar with the broad concepts of action in drug abuse situations.

Unusual, but most critical, is the emergency situation. In a case of unconsciousness, which may be drug-induced, rapid aid is vitally important. Most schools have a standing procedure for emergencies. But where none exists, a doctor should be called immediately or an ambulance should be summoned to take the victim to a hospital. If breathing fails, some form of artificial respiration should be administered until medical help arrives. Naturally, parents should be advised of the situation as quickly as possible.

The more usual situation is one in which the suspicion of drug abuse is aroused because of a student's behavior. The immediate problem, at such times, is to determine whether the student is abusing drugs or is acting peculiarly because of some condition not related to drug abuse. In this situation, medical help *must* be obtained. Should illness subsequently be ruled out, while indications of drug indulgence persist despite denials, the youngster's parents should be urged by appropriate school authorities to submit him to a more thorough examination including blood and/or urine tests—the only method for positive identification of drug abuse.

Should drug abuse be indicated through blood and urine tests (or through the admission of the youngster), parents must be made to understand the seriousness of the situation and the educator's desire to help. Because of the "contagious" nature of drug abuse, every effort should be made to determine sources of supply and names of other students who may be abusing drugs. (Experience in this area has shown that drug abusers attempt to pass their habit to friends and associates in order to raise money. For this reason the drug abuser must be identified to help avoid drug abuse spread. The frequently made claim that adult drug peddlers begin youngsters on drugs is usually contrary to fact.)

If the case proves serious, parents should be urged, by school health officials, to place their child under the care of a physician. As students with drug habits almost invariably become dropouts, continuance in an educational program may depend on the student's receiving prompt and proper medical attention. Whenever feasible, education authorities and physicians involved in such cases should maintain contact with each other to ascertain that the student is abstaining from drugs, continuing treatment, and receiving the psychological support he needs.

As the only intelligent precaution against a continuing drug problem in educational institutions requires that people in education work with law enforcement officials, the latter should be fully apprised of the situation if drug abuse is clearly established. In this connection, it is imperative that a good working relationship exist between educators and law enforcement personnel so that individual cases can be handled in the best way possible for all concerned.

A student who has been abusing drugs will probably need special educational guidance and extra emotional support. Accordingly, extraordinary efforts may be required to help him overcome his problem and stay enrolled. However, should these measures fail, the welfare of other students, who may be influenced by the presence of an active drug abuser, must be considered. In such a situation, the drug abuser may have to be referred to a special institution specifically equipped to handle such problems.

SUGGESTED PROCEDURES FOR DRUG ABUSE PREVENTION

Drug abuse prevention can be practiced effectively. Here are some rules that may be followed:

1. Basic to any drug abuse prevention program is an honest approach concerning the dangers of the problem. Learning must start early and continue throughout a student's educational years. Its nature should be informative and factual. Sermonizing *must* be avoided. The *facts* concerning the effects of drug abuse are the first steps toward enlightenment and mature behavioral value judgments.

2. The procedures for a drug abuse situation should become part of a school's written general emergency policies. These policies should delineate basic rules for handling all emergency health situations, including suspected drug abuse.

3. On the elementary and junior high school level, procedures should be established for students who must take medication during school hours for medically diagnosed health conditions. A child who must take prescription medication might be required to turn the medication over to a school nurse or doctor along with his physician's instructions for its use. The child should also be required to bring a note from his parents or guardian permitting the school to dispense the medication to him. In addition to apprising teachers that drugs in a child's possession are authorized, this procedure would keep the school better informed of the child's condition if a medical emergency should occur. Realistically speaking, however, this kind of control is rarely feasible at the high school level—and totally impractical for college-age students.

4. Because illicit drug sources for students may be outsiders (often juveniles), all visitors should be required to register at the office when entering school property—*including grounds*. Persons who "hang around" with no legitimate reason for their presence should be queried and/or reported. With few exceptions, this form of control is feasible at elementary and high schools.

5. Areas of the school that are seldom used, such as basements and storage areas, should be locked to prevent their use for illicit purposes. Parking lots and school grounds should be supervised during lunch hours and other periods when students are out of class. This type of control can be followed at elementary and secondary school levels.

6. Periodic meetings with local law enforcement authorities on drug abuse should be arranged. An understanding of each other's problems, responsibilities and limitations will promote mutual respect and smooth the way for effective cooperative activity if the occasion should arise. This kind of program should be encouraged at all educational levels.

7. In-service education, such as seminars, should be organized to keep educators and administrators at all levels fully informed of all phases of drug abuse problems.

PART VI: APPENDICES

APPENDIX A: DRUG DISTRIBUTION

Normally, the distribution flow of a drug product is as follows: from manufacturer to wholesaler to community (or hospital) pharmacy to patient. Many manufacturers also sell drug products direct to pharmacies without moving them through the wholesaler.

Drug products move from pharmacy to patient in one of two ways:

1. **Prescription Only.** Because of their potency, many drug products—including nonexempt narcotics, tranquilizers, amphetamine and barbiturates—are required by law to be sold by prescription only. Such products, called "legend drugs," carry a statement on the manufacturer's label which says: "Caution—Federal law prohibits dispensing without prescription."

2. **Over the Counter (OTC).** Some products (such as those used for relief of headache, constipation, common cold symptoms, etc.) are sold "over the counter"—that is, directly to the

consumer without a doctor's prescription. These "OTC" products are safe if directions for their use are followed. However, indiscriminate use of such products may produce adverse effects or be the precursor of later drug dependence.

Drug products capable of serious abuse can and do slip into illicit channels even though pharmacists and pharmaceutical manufacturers make stringent efforts to keep drug distribution channels secure. Here are some ways drug products fall into the wrong hands.

Illicit Operations

Some drugs not only are used illicitly, they are made illicitly. These are usually inferior drug products made by unscrupulous individuals specifically for sale to underground "buyers." Many of these clandestine "manufacturers" operate in garages, basements, abandoned warehouses—anywhere they can set up a manufacturing operation without being detected.

Another kind of illicit operation is that conducted by "front organizations"—individuals posing as legitimate distributors to obtain *bona fide* medicines for distribution mainly to illicit buyers. Responsible drug manufacturers carefully investigate distributors of their products to be certain they are of impeccable reputation.

Smuggling

The most important narcotic from the standpoint of illicit trade—heroin—is completely outlawed in the United States and most other countries as well. It can neither be imported, manufactured nor sold legally in this country. Hence, its entry into the illegal market is always through smuggling, the operation of which is controlled by vast criminal syndicates. Most heroin comes from opium made from poppies grown illicitly in Turkey, Afghanistan, Mexico and Southeast Asia. Opium grown in Turkey is smuggled through Lebanon to France or Syria where the raw product is refined into heroin for distribution all over the world. The bulk of it, however, is smuggled into the United States and Canada.

Because of the severe restrictions in force against marihuana, most of it seen in the United States has been smuggled in from Mexico over a thinly patrolled border. Another variety of marihuana, much stronger than the Mexican type, comes from the Near East, Middle East and Africa. Called hashish, it is rarely encountered in this country owing to the widespread availability of the relatively inexpensive Mexican variety. Hashish has been strictly controlled by international law since 1961.

Bulk Peddlers

The "bulk peddler" can enter the chain of drug distribution at any point. He may obtain his supplies from unscrupulous distributors, illicit manufacturers or smugglers. He deals in hundreds of thousands of capsules and tablets, selling them to bars, truck stops, "diet mills," newsstands and restaurants.

Obtaining Drug Products by Fraud

While many drug abusers depend on illicit sources of supply, others obtain drugs by defrauding legitimate supply sources. For example, an abuser might steal a physician's prescription pad, forge a prescription and take it to a pharmacy, where the pharmacist unknowingly fills it for him. Or, he might alter a legitimate prescription—usually by writing in a greater quantity of tablets or capsules. Some abusers even go so far as to read medical texts on certain ailments requiring abusable drugs for treatment. Armed with this information, these individuals go to doctors and recite the proper history of complaints. The unwary physicians then write prescriptions for abusable products.

Illegal Sales by Pharmacists and Physicians

Each year, a small number of pharmacists and physicians are arrested for illegal sale of abusable drug products. However, professional misconduct accounts for an extremely small part of the drug abuse picture. For example, the Food and Drug Administration recorded only 51 such prosecutions from July 1, 1965, to June 30, 1966. (There are more than 250,000 physicians and about 53,000 retail pharmacies in the country.)

Other Sources for the Illicit Market

Although they are not significant in the overall picture, the following factors also contribute to the illicit market: plant pilferage; individual scavenging operations in which a plant's discarded boxes and barrels are examined for saleable products; acquisition, by unscrupulous individuals, of the stock of bankrupt pharmacies (usually through deception); and theft of shipments in transit.

APPENDIX B: LEGAL CONTROLS

Narcotic Controls

The chief Federal law for controlling illicit narcotic traffic is still the Harrison Act. Another important law is the Marihuana Tax Act of 1937 (pharmacologically, marihuana is not a narcotic, but it is controlled by the Federal Bureau of Narcotics). Modeled after the Harrison Act, this law was enacted both because of treaty obligations and because use of marihuana (though non-addicting) frequently precedes use of heroin or other "hard" narcotics. Like its model, the marihuana act and its amendments assess severe penalties on illegal buyers and sellers.

These are the important features of the Harrison Act and other Federal narcotics laws:

1. Registration (filing name and address with a Federal agency) of individuals and firms which manufacture, buy or sell narcotics.

2. The impost of special taxes on narcotics buyers and sellers.

3. Requirements for special record-keeping by those dealing with narcotics.

4. Provision for severe penalties for illicit sale or possession of narcotic drugs.

Penalties under Federal narcotic laws are severe. For example, illegal *sale* of narcotics can result in a $20,000 fine and a 5- to 20-year prison term for the first offense. Subsequent offenses call for the same fine and a 10- to 40-year prison term. When sale of heroin is made to a person under 18, parole and probation are denied, even for a first offense. The penalty can be a life term or even death.

Penalties for other narcotic offenses are less severe. For example, illegal *possession* of narcotics is punishable by fines and/or imprisonment for 2 to 10 years for the first offense, 5 to 20 years for the second, and 10 to 20 years for subsequent offenses. Parole and probation are denied after a first offense.

Between 1927 and 1932, the Commission on Uniform State Laws and the Federal Bureau of Narcotics prepared a Uniform Narcotics Law for controlling narcotic traffic at the state level. Today, most states have adopted a version of that law. Penalties vary from state to state, but otherwise state laws conform closely to the Federal law.

Not all narcotic preparations are treated alike. Some narcotic-containing medicines, classified under the law as "exempt" preparations, can be sold without a doctor's prescription. The narcotic content of these medicines (usually cough syrups) is very low. At present, some states require a prescription or limit the amount sold to one person within a 24- to 48-hour period. In a few states, the buyer must be over 21 years of age in order to get these drug products without a doctor's prescription.

Depressant and Stimulant Controls

The primary Federal law for controlling traffic in depressants and stimulants is the Drug Abuse Control Amendments of 1965. Prior to passage, these amendments received strong endorsement from the executive branch of the Federal government, representatives of consumers, and the pharmaceutical industry. President Lyndon B. Johnson personally endorsed the bill, and its passage was virtually unanimous.

In effect since February 1, 1966, this act, administered by the Department of Health, Education, and Welfare, imposes these requirements:
1. That all wholesalers, jobbers and manufacturers of controlled drugs must register annually with the Food and Drug Administration and keep records of controlled drugs.

2. That pharmacists, hospitals and doctors who regularly dispense and charge for controlled drugs must keep records of all transactions.

In addition, the act prohibits:
1. Refilling a prescription for one of these drugs more than five times or later than six months after it was originally written.

2. Manufacturing, processing and compounding the designated drugs, except by registered drug firms.

3. Distributing the designated drugs to persons not authorized to receive them by Federal or state law.

Penalties for a first-offense under the Drug Abuse Control Amendments can be a $1,000 fine or up to a year in jail, or both. Subsequent offenses can be punishable by a $10,000 fine or up to three years in jail, or both. The law contains special penalties for those convicted of selling controlled drugs to persons under 21 years of age. These penalties range up to a $5,000 fine or two years in prison or both for a first offense, and a $15,000 fine or six years in prison or both for subsequent offenses.

State legislation dealing with non-narcotic drugs is anything but uniform. While all states have some type of regulations covering prescription drugs, many also have special laws specifically regulating barbiturates and amphetamine. The current trend is to remodel old laws or adopt new ones that conform closely to the Drug Abuse Control Amendments.

APPENDIX C: WHERE TO GET HELP

Most drug abuse situations will not require emergency medical help. They will, however, raise many perplexing medical questions which educators will want answered. For information relating to a specific situation, or to drug abuse in general, the educator will naturally turn to his school doctor or another local physician. In addition, he may contact the city or county medical society listed in his phone directory. Other possibilities are local and state public health agencies. Many of these organizations will be able to provide direct assistance or names of physicians who may be consulted.

From a law enforcement standpoint, schools should have a pre-arranged procedure with their local police for handling drug abuse situations. This will generally mean that, should such a situation be detected, school authorities will contact the narcotics squad commander or appropriate official of the local police department or sheriff's office. In some areas, arrangements may have to be made with the nearest barracks of the state police or through state police headquarters, usually in state capitals. For answers to legal questions, state attorney generals or departments of justice can often render assistance.

In some situations or localities, it may be more convenient to contact the Food and Drug Administration or Bureau of Narcotics. These agencies offer general information regarding drug abuse, including written material. Illegal sales of barbiturates and amphetamine should be reported to the FDA's Bureau of Drug Abuse Control which maintains a number of regional offices. (See next page.) If drugs such as opium, heroin, morphine or marihuana are involved, the report should be made to the Federal Bureau of Narcotics which also maintains regional offices. (See page 84.)

LIST I

BUREAU OF DRUG ABUSE CONTROL
221 Jefferson Davis Highway
Washington, D.C. 20204

ATLANTA FIELD OFFICE
441 W. Peachtree St., N.W.,
Room 406
Atlanta, Georgia 30308
404-526-6485
  Alabama, Florida, Georgia,
  Mississippi, South Carolina,
  Tennessee

BALTIMORE FIELD OFFICE
401 Water Street
Baltimore, Maryland 21202
301-752-2631
  District of Columbia, Kentucky,
  Maryland, North Carolina,
  Virginia, West Virginia

BOSTON FIELD OFFICE
114 Federal Street
Boston, Massachusetts 02110
617-223-6632
  Connecticut, Maine, Massachusetts,
  New Hampshire, Rhode Island,
  Vermont

CHICAGO FIELD OFFICE
205 W. Wacker Drive
Room 1700 Engineering Building
Chicago, Illinois 60606
312-828-5850/51/52
  Illinois, Indiana, Michigan,
  Ohio, Wisconsin

DALLAS FIELD OFFICE
1114 Commerce Street
Dallas, Texas 75207
214-749-3917
  Arkansas, Louisiana, Oklahoma,
  New Mexico, Texas

DENVER FIELD OFFICE
1814 California Street
Denver, Colorado 80202
303-297-4291
  Colorado, Idaho, Montana,
  Utah, Wyoming

KANSAS CITY FIELD OFFICE
U.S. Courthouse, Room 803
811 Grand Avenue
Kansas City, Missouri 64106
816-374-5604
  Iowa, Kansas, Minnesota,
  Missouri, Nebraska, North
  Dakota, South Dakota

LOS ANGELES FIELD OFFICE
714 W. Olympic Boulevard,
Room 1010
Los Angeles, California 90015
213-688-2650
  Alaska, Arizona, California, Hawaii,
  Nevada, Oregon, Washington

NEW YORK FIELD OFFICE
346 Broadway, 12th Floor
New York, New York 10013
212-264-8457/58
  Delaware, New Jersey, New York,
  Pennsylvania, Puerto Rico,
  Virgin Islands

LIST II

BUREAU OF NARCOTICS

United States Treasury Department
Washington, D.C.

DISTRICT OFFICES

District	Territory	Headquarters
1	Maine, New Hampshire, Vermont, Rhode Island, Massachusetts and Connecticut	1425 Post Office and Courthouse Building Boston, Massachusetts 02109
2	New York State and the Newark District of New Jersey	90 Church Street, Suite 605 New York, New York 10007
3	Pennsylvania, Delaware and Camden District of New Jersey	605 U.S. Custom House Philadelphia, Pennsylvania 19106
5	Maryland, District of Columbia, North Carolina, Virginia and West Virginia	103 South Gay Street, Room 301 Baltimore, Maryland 21202
6	Georgia, Florida, Alabama, South Carolina and Tennessee	1056 Federal Office Building Atlanta, Georgia 30303
8	Michigan, Kentucky and Ohio	602 Federal Building Detroit, Michigan 48226
9	Illinois, Indiana and Wisconsin	1836 U.S. Courthouse and Federal Office Building Chicago, Illinois 60604
10	Texas, Louisiana and Mississippi	1114 Commerce Street Dallas, Texas 75202
11	Missouri, Kansas, Arkansas and Oklahoma	1502 Federal Office Building Kansas City, Missouri 64106
12	Minnesota, Iowa, Nebraska, North Dakota and South Dakota	402 Federal Building Minneapolis, Minnesota 55401
13	Colorado, Utah, Wyoming and New Mexico	106 U.S. Custom House Denver, Colorado 80202
14	California, Nevada and Arizona	450 Golden Gate Avenue San Francisco, California 94102
15	Washington, Oregon, Idaho, Montana, Alaska and Hawaii	311 U.S. Courthouse Seattle, Washington 98104

APPENDIX D: SELECTED FILMS

The following films have been previewed by the editors and found acceptable in terms of technical and informational qualities. However, since classes—even in the same grades—vary considerably in maturity, level of interest and response to instruction, teachers should carefully screen each film prior to presentation.

Before ordering, and well in advance of the contemplated showing date, teachers should write or call the distributor for information about film availability and rental arrangements.

The Dangerous Drugs

The Narcotic Educational Foundation of America, 1960

22 min., color or b & w

High school through college

The Narcotic Educational Foundation of America
5055 Sunset Boulevard
Los Angeles, Calif. 90027

Sale: Color: $235
B & W: $125
Rental: Color: $12.50 per day
B & W: $6.00 per day

This film vividly portrays the dangers from abuse of amphetamine and barbiturate drugs: accidents, physical dependence (from barbiturates), ruined health, even death. A candid account by a female abuser dramatically and forcefully underscores the points made in the preceding vignettes. The potential relationship of heroin abuse and abuse of non-narcotic drugs is noted.

Hide & Seek

Columbia University Press, 1966

14 min., color

Junior high school through college

Center for Mass Communication
Columbia University Press
1125 Amsterdam Avenue
New York, N. Y. 10025

Sale: $150
Rental: Inquire

Highly recommended. Film depicts, with excellent photographic technique, the anguish and despair of a teen-ager caught by the narcotic habit and unable to shake it. In narration, the victim relates his helplessness and the realization that he has unwittingly committed himself to a joyless and hopeless existence. The events shown in the film are actual experiences, with the narration by the addict himself.

Hooked

Churchill Films, 1965	Sale: Churchill Films
	662 N. Robertson Boulevard
20 min., b & w	Los Angeles, Calif. 90069
	$125
	Rental: Indiana University
	Audio-Visual Center
	Bloomington, Ind. 47401
Junior high school through college	$4.65

Excellent film. Young people (ages 18 to 25), in what appears to be a security institution, describe their experiences with drug addiction. The descriptions are uninhibited, sometimes shocking, and make frequent use of addicts' jargon. The young people speak with candor about what impelled them to use drugs, how drug abuse affected their relationships with others, and the disgust with which they now regard their drug experiences.

The Losers

WCBS-TV, New York, 1965	Sale: Carousel Films, Inc.
	1501 Broadway
31 min., b & w	New York, N. Y. 10036
	$145
	Rental: United Church of Christ
	Office of Audio-Visuals
	1501 Race Street
	Philadelphia, Pa. 19102
	Yeshiva University
	Audio-Visual Center
	526 West 187th Street
	New York, N. Y. 10033
	Association Films, Inc.
	347 Madison Avenue
Junior high through high school	New York, N. Y. 10017

Fine exposition of the drug abuse problem in relation to teen-agers. Film examines the prevalence and habitual use of chemicals and drugs among young people from 12 to 21. Actual experiences are recounted by youths from both slums and "nice" neighborhoods. Although it deals with the problem in New York City, this kinescope of a TV program makes points applicable anywhere. Especially noteworthy is a clear presentation of the harmful effects of glue-sniffing, and the use of marihuana, stimulants, depressants and heroin.

Narcotics: A Challenge

The Narcotic Educational
Foundation of America, 1963

24 min., color or b & w

For educators on junior and senior
high school and college levels

The Narcotic Educational
Foundation of America
5055 Sunset Boulevard
Los Angeles, Calif. 90027

Sale: Color: $275
      B & W: $140
Rental: Color: $12.50 per day
      B & W: $7.50 per day

This film is directed at educators. Narrated by Lowell Thomas, it provides basic information about narcotics and other drugs of abuse. The film challenges educators to combat student drug abuse by presenting young people with the *facts* about drug experimentation. Although the setting is a high school, the film should also be of interest to college educators. After viewing, teachers may wish to show the film to students.

Narcotics: The Decision

United Research and
Training, Inc., 1960

30 min., color or b & w

Study guide

High school students

Film Distributors International
2223 S. Olive Street
Los Angeles, Calif. 90007

Sale: Color: $265
      B & W: $145
Rental: $15

This film tells a dramatic story of a teen-age girl who is trapped into drug addiction. Not a pleasant film, but one that should have strong impact on high school students, it includes ugly scenes of needle administration of heroin and symptoms of withdrawal. Although some concepts in the film are no longer generally accepted—the inevitable progression from marihuana to heroin, and the idea that pushers always prey on unsuspecting youngsters—the total effect overcomes these inaccuracies.

Narcotics—Why Not

Charles Cahill and
Associates, Inc., 1966

15 min., color or b & w

Sale: Charles Cahill and Associates, Inc.
P. O. Box 3220
Hollywood, Calif. 90028
Color: $175
B & W: $90

Rental: Krasker Memorial Film Library
Boston University School of
Education
765 Commonwealth Avenue
Boston, Mass. 02215

University of Southern California
Department of Cinema
Film Distribution Division
University Park
Los Angeles, Calif. 90007

Indiana University
Film Rental Library
Audio Visual Center
Bloomington, Ind. 47401

Junior high through college

$6.15

An impressive film which presents a series of extemporaneous interviews with male and female residents of the California Rehabilitation Center. Both teen-agers and young adults relate how they were introduced to glue, stimulants and depressants, marihuana and heroin. They tell what it is like to be under the influence of dangerous drugs, discuss their regrets, and examine their hopes for the future. A realistic film which has an impact that could not be achieved by using actors.

The Riddle

Quest Productions, 1966

20 min., b & w

Junior high through college

Inquiries for rental:

Public Affairs
Office of Economic Opportunity
1200 19th Street, N.W.
Washington, D. C. 20506

An exceptional film—utilizing documentary technique—which strips drug abuse of any vestiges of glamor. The camera follows actual glue sniffers, cough medicine drinkers and heroin addicts into the alleys, tenements and physicians' offices where their candid comments and bewildered responses clearly show the hopelessness of their lives. By contrast, an account of a youth who resists the drug abuse crowd to land a job strikes a hopeful note. The fast-cut film technique and rock and roll sound track during part of the footage hold audience interest. A powerful film, it will be considered shocking by many.

Seduction of the Innocent

Sid Davis Productions, 1961

10 min., color or b & w

Sale: Sid Davis Productions
1418 N. Highland Ave.
Hollywood, Calif. 90028
Color: $120
B & W: $60

Rental: University of Wyoming
Audio-Visual Services
Laramie, Wyo. 82070
Attn: Booking Clerk

Audio-Visual Center
Indiana University
Bloomington, Ind. 47401

Senior high school through college

Color: $3.90

A hard-hitting film, sometimes overly dramatic, about a teen-age boy and girl who progress from barbiturates and amphetamine to marihuana and then heroin. The film focuses on the girl and her desperate efforts to raise money for her habit—leading ultimately to prostitution and arrest. Although the story utilizes the scare technique, and is heavy with drug abuse clichés, it points out the dangers inherent in drug experimentation.

APPENDIX E:
SELECTED BOOKS, PAMPHLETS AND ARTICLES

Books

1. Anslinger, H.J., and Tompkins, W.F.: *The Traffic in Narcotics*, Funk and Wagnalls, New York, 1953.

2. Casriel, D.: *So Fair a House: The Story of Synanon*, Prentice-Hall, Inc., Englewood Cliffs, New Jersey, 1963.

3. Connell, P.H.: *Amphetamine Psychosis*, Chapman & Hall, Ltd., London, 1958.

4. Chein, I., et al.: *The Road to H*, Basic Books, Inc., New York, 1964.

5. *Drug Addiction: Crime or Disease?* Interim and Final Reports of the American Bar Association and the American Medical Association on Narcotic Drugs, Indiana University Press, Bloomington, 1963.

6. Ebin, D., ed.: *The Drug Experience*, Orion Press, 1961, Evergreen Black Cat Edition, New York, 1965.

7. Eldridge, W.B.: *Narcotics and the Law*, New York University Press (Distributor), New York, 1962.

8. Harms, E.: *Drug Addiction in Youth*, Pergamon Press, Inc., New York, 1965.

9. Maurer, D.W., and Vogel, V.H.: *Narcotics and Narcotic Addiction*, Charles C Thomas, 2nd Ed., Springfield, Ill., 1962.

10. Mayor's Committee on Marihuana: *The Marihuana Problem in the City of New York; Sociological, Medical, Psychological and Pharmacological Studies*, Jaques Cattell Press, Lancaster, Pa., 1944.

11. Ross, B., and Abramson, M.: *No Man Stands Alone: The True Story of Barney Ross*, J.B. Lippincott Company, Philadelphia, 1957.

12. Street, L.: *I Was a Drug Addict*, Random House, Inc., New York, 1953.

13. Wilner, D.M., and Kassebaum, G.G.: *Narcotics*, McGraw-Hill, Inc., New York, 1965.

14. Yablonsky, L.: *The Tunnel Back: Synanon*, MacMillan Co., New York, 1965.

Pamphlets and Government Publications

1. *Barbiturates as Addicting Drugs*, Public Health Service Publication No. 545 (revised June, 1963).

2. Department of Mental Health of AMA: *Narcotics Addiction. Official Actions of the American Medical Association*, published by AMA, 1963.

3. *Drug Abuse: The Empty Life*, Smith Kline & French Laboratories, Philadelphia, Pa., 1965.

4. *Fact Sheet—Drug Abuse Control Amendments of 1965*, Public Law 89-74, 89th Congress, U.S. Dept. HEW, FDA, 1965.

5. **Medicinal Narcotics*, Pharmaceutical Manufacturers Association, Washington, D.C., 1965.

6. *Mental Health Monograph 2: *Narcotic Drug Addiction*, Public Health Service Publication No. 1021, 1965.

7. Mental Health Monograph 3: *Rehabilitation in Drug Addiction. A Report on a Five-Year Community Experiment of the New York Demonstration Center*, Public Health Service Publication No. 1013 (revised 1964).

8. *Proceedings—White House Conference on Narcotics and Drug Abuse*, September 27 and 28, 1962, U.S. Government Printing Office, Washington, D.C.

9. *The President's Advisory Commission on Narcotic and Drug Abuse: Final Report*, November, 1963, U.S. Government Printing Office, Washington, D.C.

10. *Student Reference Sheet: *Hallucinogenic Drugs*, U.S. Dept. HEW, FDA, 1965.

11. *Vogel, V.H., and Vogel, V.E.: *Facts about Narcotics*, Chicago, Illinois, Science Research Associates, Inc. (Guidance Series Booklets—Reorder No. 5-805), 1951.

12. Winick, C., and Goldstein, J.: *The Glue Sniffing Problem*, published by the American Social Health Association, New York, New York.

13. U.S. Treasury Department, Bureau of Narcotics: *Prevention and Control of Narcotic Addiction*, Government Printing Office, 1964.

*Recommended for reading by high school or college students—as well as instructors.

Articles in Medical and Scientific Journals

1. Ausubel, D.P.: Causes and Types of Narcotic Addiction: A Psychosocial View, Psychiatric Quart. 34:523 (July) 1961.

2. Barron, F., et al.: The Hallucinogenic Drugs, Scient. Am. 210:29 (April) 1964.

3. Berger, H.: Treatment of Narcotic Addicts in Private Practice, Arch. Int. Med. 114:59 (July) 1964.

4. Bloomquist, E.R.: Let's Think Twice About "Free" Narcotics, GP 21: 156 (May) 1960; 21:149 (June) 1960.

5. Brill, H.: Misapprehensions about Drug Addiction: Some Origins and Repercussions, Comprehen. Psychiat. 4:150 (June) 1964.

6. Brotman, R., et al.: An Approach to Treating Narcotic Addicts Based on a Community Mental Health Diagnosis, Comprehen. Psychiat. 6:104 (April) 1965.

7. Cohen, S.: A Classification of LSD Complications, Psychosomatics 7:182 (May-June) 1966.

8. Committee on Alcoholism and Addiction and Council on Mental Health: Dependence on Barbiturates and Other Sedative Drugs, J.A.M.A. 193:673 (August 23) 1965.

9. Committee on Alcoholism and Addiction and Council on Mental Health: Dependence on Amphetamines and Other Stimulant Drugs, J.A.M.A. 197:1023 (September 19) 1966.

10. Dalrymple, W.: A Doctor Speaks of Marihuana and Other "Drugs," J. Am. Coll. Health Assoc. 14:218 (February) 1966.

11. Diskind, M.H., and Klonsky, G.: A Second Look at the New York State Parole Drug Experiment, Federal Probation 28:34, 1964.

12. Eddy, N.B., et al.: Drug Dependence: Its Significance and Characteristics, Bull. World Health Organ. 32:721, 1965.

13. Esty, G.W.: Preventing Drug Addiction Through Education, Public Health News 47:87 (April) 1966.

14. Hess, C.B.: New Trends in Narcotic Addiction Control, Public Health Reports 81:277 (March) 1966.

15. Hoffer, A.: D-lysergic Acid Diethylamide (LSD): A Review of Its Present Status, Clin. Pharmacol. & Therap. 6:183 (March-April) 1965.

16. Jermulowicz, Z.W., and Turnau, Mag. A.: Control and Treatment of Drug Addicts in Israel, Bull. Narcotics 14:11 (April-June) 1962.

17. Kleber, H.D.: Student Use of Hallucinogens, J. Am. Coll. Health Assoc. 14:109, 1965.

18. Moraes, A.O.: The Criminogenic Action of Cannabis (Marihuana) and Narcotics, Bull. Narcotics 16:23 (October-December) 1964.

19. Murphy, H.B.M.: The Cannabis Habit: A Review of Recent Psychiatric Literature, Bull. Narcotics 15:15 (January-March) 1963.

20. Osnos, R.J.B.: The Treatment of Narcotics Addiction, New York J. Med. 63:1182 (April 15) 1963.

21. Osnos, R.: A Community Counseling Center for Addicts, Nurs. Outlook 13:38 (November) 1965.

22. Seevers, M.H.: Abuse of Barbiturates and Amphetamines, Postgrad. M. J. 37:45 (January) 1965.

23. Shelley, J.A., and Bassin, A.: Daytop Lodge—A New Treatment Approach for Drug Addicts, Corrective Psychiatry and J. of Social Therapy 11:186 (July) 1965.

24. Vaillant, G.E.: A Twelve-Year Follow-Up of New York Narcotic Addicts: I. The Relation of Treatment to Outcome, Am. J. Psychiat. 122:727 (January) 1966.

25. Weech, A.A., Jr.: The Narcotic Addict and "The Street," Arch. Gen. Psychiat. 14:299 (March) 1966.

26. Wilbur, M., and Connor, T.: Intensive Casework with Drug Addicts, Case Conference 12:388 (April) 1966.

NOTE: Additional references for books, pamphlets and articles may be secured from the National Institute of Mental Health, Bethesda, Maryland 20014. Requests should be made for *Current Reading List on Mental Health*, *Bibliography on Barbiturate Addiction*, and the various bibliographies on narcotic drug addiction.

KEY TO ABBREVIATIONS

Am. J. Psychiat.	American Journal of Psychiatry
Arch. Gen. Psychiat.	Archives of General Psychiatry
Arch. Int. Med.	Archives of Internal Medicine
Bull. Narcotics	Bulletin of Narcotics
Bull. World Health Organ.	Bulletin of the World Health Organization
Clin. Pharmacol. & Therap.	Clinical Pharmacology and Therapeutics
Comprehen. Psychiat.	Comprehensive Psychiatry
J. Am. Coll. Health Assoc.	Journal of the American College Health Association
J.A.M.A.	Journal of the American Medical Association
New York J. Med.	New York State Journal of Medicine
Nurs. Outlook	Nursing Outlook
Postgrad. M. J.	Postgraduate Medical Journal
Psychiatric Quart.	Psychiatric Quarterly
Scient. Am.	Scientific American

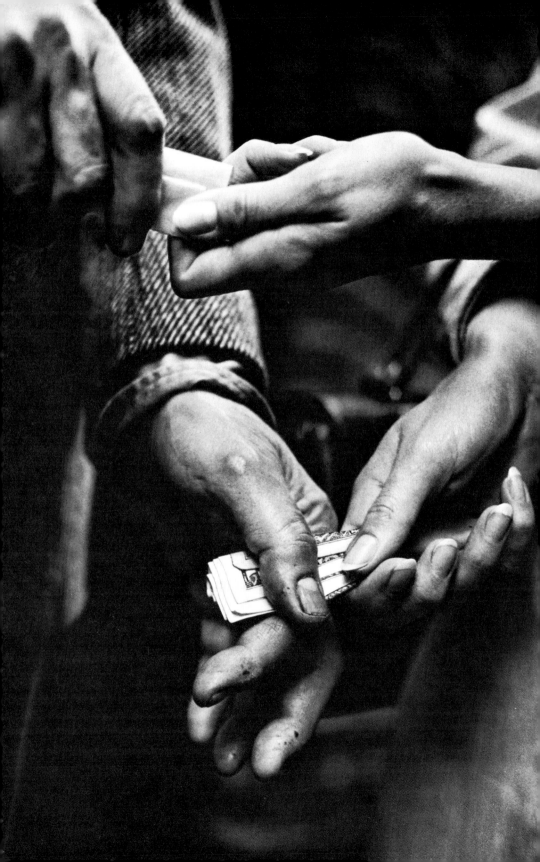

PART VII: TECHNICAL DEFINITIONS AND GLOSSARY OF SLANG TERMS

TECHNICAL TERMS

1. **Addiction** In 1957, the World Health Organization (WHO) defined drug addiction as a state of periodic or chronic intoxication produced by the repeated consumption of a drug. Its characteristics include: (1) an overpowering desire or need (compulsion) to continue taking the drug and to obtain it by any means; (2) a tendency to increase the dose; (3) a psychic (psychological) and generally a physical dependence on the effects of the drug; (4) an effect detrimental to the individual and to society.

2. **Central Nervous System** The brain and spinal cord.

3. **Convulsions** An involuntary and violent irregular series of contractions of the muscles.

4. **Delirium** A condition characterized by mental excitement, confusion, disordered speech and, often, hallucinations.

5. **Depressant** Any of several drugs which sedate by acting on the central nervous system. Medical uses include the treatment of anxiety, tension and high blood pressure.

6. **Drug Dependence** As described in 1963 by WHO, drug dependence is "a state arising from repeated administration of a drug on a periodic or continuous basis." Its characteristics will vary with the agent involved. This is made clear by designating the particular type of drug dependence in each specific case—for example, drug dependence of the morphine type, of the cocaine type, of the cannabis type, of the barbiturate type, etc.

7. **Habituation** As defined in 1957 by WHO, drug habituation is a condition, resulting from the repeated consumption of a drug, which includes these characteristics: (1) a desire (but not a compulsion) to continue taking the drug for the sense of improved well-being that it engenders; (2) little or no tendency to increase the dose; (3) some degree of psychic dependence on the effect of the drug, but absence of physical dependence and, hence, no abstinence syndrome; (4) a detrimental effect, if any, primarily on the individual.

8. **Hallucinogen** Any of several drugs, popularly called psychedelics, which produce sensations such as distortions of time, space, sound, color and other bizarre effects. While they are pharmacologically non-narcotic, some of these drugs (e.g., marihuana) are regulated under Federal narcotic laws.

9. **Hypnotic** An agent that induces sleep.

10. **Narcotic** This term has two definitions. Medically defined, a narcotic is any drug that produces sleep or stupor and also relieves pain. Legally defined, the term means any drug regulated under the Harrison Act and other Federal narcotic laws. Some of these regulated drugs are pharmacologically non-narcotic (e.g., cocaine).

11. **Potentiation** Potentiation occurs when the combined action of two or more drugs is greater than the sum of the effects of each drug taken alone. Potentiation can be very useful in certain medical procedures. For example, physicians can induce and maintain a specific degree of anesthesia with a small amount of the primary anesthetic agent by using another drug to potentiate the primary anesthetic agent. Potentiation may also be danger-

ous. For example, barbiturates and many tranquilizers potentiate the depressant effects of alcohol.

12. Physical Dependence Physiological adaptation of the body to the presence of a drug. In effect, the body develops a continuing need for the drug. Once such dependence has been established, the body reacts with predictable symptoms if the drug is abruptly withdrawn. The nature and severity of withdrawal symptoms depend on the drug being used and the daily dosage level attained.

13. Psychological Dependence An attachment to drug use which arises from a drug's ability to satisfy some emotional or personality need of an individual. This attachment does not require a physical dependence, although physical dependence may seem to reinforce psychological dependence. An individual may also be psychologically dependent on substances other than drugs.

14. Psychosis A major mental disorder; any serious mental derangement. "Psychosis" replaces the old term "insanity."

15. Sedative An agent which quiets or calms activity.

16. Side Effects A given drug may have many actions on the body. Usually one or two of the more prominent actions will be medically useful. The others, usually weaker effects, are called side effects. They are not necessarily harmful, but may be annoying.

17. Stimulant Any of several drugs which act on the central nervous system, producing excitation, alertness and wakefulness. Medical uses include the treatment of mild depressive states, overweight and narcolepsy—a disease characterized by an almost overwhelming desire to sleep.

18. Tolerance With many drugs, a person must keep increasing the dosage to maintain the same effect. This characteristic is called tolerance. Tolerance develops with the barbiturates, with amphetamine and related compounds, and with opiates.

19. Toxic Effects (poisoning) Any substance in excessive amounts can act as a poison or toxin. With drugs, the margin between the dosage that produces beneficial effects and dosage that produces toxic or poisonous effects varies greatly. Moreover, this margin will vary with the person taking the drug.

SLANG TERMS

In the world of drug abuse, there is a special language, a descriptively rich shorthand, that covers almost every aspect of the abuser's life as affected by his habit.

Part "hip," part the language of those who live outside the law, the jargon of the abuser is often a tip-off to his preoccupation: drugs and how to get them.

There are, of course, variations in this lexicon as one moves from one part of the country to another. In addition, it is a language which changes often, both in nuance and in terms. Often, the language of drug abuse is picked up as contemporary slang by non-abusers—particularly teen-agers. For this reason, use of many of these terms can't be considered evidence of drug abuse.

What follows is a compilation from several sources. It is not all inclusive, but it is indicative of what they're saying "on the street."

Acid—LSD
Acid head—an abuser of LSD
Artillery—equipment for injecting drugs

Backtrack—to withdraw the plunger of a syringe before injecting drugs to make sure needle is in proper position
Bag—a container of drugs
Bagman—a drug supplier
Bang—to inject drugs
Barbs—barbiturates
Bennies—'Benzedrine' (brand of amphetamine sulfate, Smith Kline & French Laboratories) tablets
Bernice—cocaine
Big John—the police
Bindle—a small quantity or packet of narcotics
Biz—equipment for injecting drugs
Blanks—poor quality narcotics
Blasted—under the influence of drugs
Blow a stick—to smoke a marihuana cigarette
Blue devils—'Amytal' (brand of amobarbital, Eli Lilly and Company) capsules
Blue velvet—paregoric and an antihistamine
Bombido—injectable amphetamine

Boxed—in jail

Bread—money

Bull—a Federal narcotic agent, a police officer

Burned—to receive phony or badly diluted drugs

Busted—arrested

Candy—barbiturates

Cap—a container of drugs (usually, a capsule)

Cartwheels—amphetamine sulfate (round, white, double-scored tablets)

Champ—drug abuser who won't reveal his supplier—even under pressure

Charged up—under the influence of drugs

Chipping—taking small amounts of drugs on an irregular basis

Chippy—an abuser taking small, irregular amounts—also, prostitute

Clear up—to withdraw from drugs

Coasting—under the influence of drugs

Coke—cocaine

Cokie—a cocaine addict

Cold turkey—sudden drug withdrawal

Connect—to purchase drugs

Connection—a drug supplier

Cook up a pill—to prepare opium for smoking

Co-pilots—amphetamine tablets

Cop—to purchase drugs

Cop-out—to alibi, confess

Corine—cocaine

Cotics—narcotics

Cut—to adulterate a narcotic by adding milksugar

Dabble—to take small amounts of drugs on an irregular basis

Dealer—a drug supplier

Deck—a small packet of narcotics

Dexies—'Dexedrine' (brand of dextroamphetamine sulfate, Smith Kline & French Laboratories) tablets

Dime bag—a ten-dollar purchase of narcotics

Dollies—'Dolophine' (brand of methadone hydrochloride, Eli Lilly and Company) tablets

Domino—to purchase drugs

Dope—any narcotic

Double trouble—'Tuinal' (brand of amobarbital sodium and seco-
    barbital sodium, Eli Lilly and Company) capsules
Dropped—arrested
Dust—cocaine

Factory—equipment for injecting drugs
Fix—an injection of narcotics
Flake—cocaine
Flea powder—poor quality narcotics
Floating—under the influence of drugs
Footballs—oval-shaped amphetamine sulfate tablets
Fresh and sweet—out of jail
Fuzz—the police

Gage—marihuana
Gee-head—paregoric abuser
Geetis—money
Geezer—a narcotic injection
Gimmicks—the equipment for injecting drugs
Gold dust—cocaine
Goods—narcotics
Goofballs—barbiturates
Gow-head—an opium addict
Grass—marihuana
Greenies—green, heart-shaped tablets of dextroamphetamine
    sulfate and amobarbital
Griefo—marihuana
Gun—a hypodermic needle

H—heroin
Hang-up—a personal problem
Hard stuff—morphine, cocaine or heroin
Harry—heroin
Hay—marihuana
Hearts—'Benzedrine' or 'Dexedrine' (brands of amphetamine
    sulfate and dextroamphetamine sulfate,
    Smith Kline & French Laboratories)
    heart-shaped tablets
Heat—the police
Hemp—marihuana

High—under the influence of drugs
Hit—to purchase drugs, an arrest
Hocus—a narcotic solution ready for injection
Hooked—addicted
Hophead—narcotic addict
Hopped up—under the influence of drugs
Horse—heroin
Hot—wanted by police
Hot shot—a fatal dosage
Hype—narcotic addict

Ice cream habit—a small, irregular drug habit

Job—to inject drugs
Jive—marihuana
Joint—a marihuana cigarette
Joy-pop—to inject small amounts of drugs irregularly
Joy powder—heroin
Junk—narcotics
Junkie—a narcotic addict

Kick—to abandon a drug habit

Layout—the equipment for injecting drugs
Lid proppers—amphetamine
Lipton tea—poor quality narcotics
Lit up—under the influence of drugs
Locoweed—marihuana

Machinery—equipment for injecting drugs
Mainline—to inject drugs directly into a vein
Make a buy—to purchase drugs
Make a meet—to purchase drugs
Man—the police
Manicure—high-grade marihuana (i.e., no seeds or stems)
Mary Jane—marihuana
Mezz—marihuana
Mickey Finn—chloral hydrate
Miss Emma—morphine
Mojo—narcotics
Monkey—a drug habit where physical dependence is present

Mor a grifa—marihuana
Mutah—marihuana

Needle—hypodermic syringe
Nickel bag—a five-dollar purchase of narcotics
Nimby—'Nembutal' (brand of pentobarbital,
    Abbott Laboratories) capsules

Off—withdrawn from drugs
On a trip—under the influence of LSD or other hallucinogens
On the nod—under the influence of drugs
On the street—out of jail
Oranges—'Dexedrine' (brand of dextroamphetamine sulfate,
    Smith Kline & French Laboratories) tablets

Paper—a prescription or packet of narcotics
Peaches—'Benzedrine' (brand of amphetamine sulfate,
    Smith Kline & French Laboratories) tablets
Peanuts—barbiturates
P.G. or P.O.—paregoric
Piece—a container of drugs
Pinks—'Seconal' (brand of secobarbital, Eli Lilly and Company)
    capsules
Plant—a cache of narcotics
Pop—to inject drugs
Pot—marihuana

Quill—a folded matchbox cover from which narcotics are sniffed
    through the nose

Rainbows—'Tuinal' (brand of amobarbital sodium and secobar-
    bital sodium, Eli Lilly and Company) capsules
Reader—a prescription
Red devils—'Seconal' (brand of secobarbital,
    Eli Lilly and Company) capsules
Reefer—a marihuana cigarette
Roach—the butt of a marihuana cigarette
Rope—marihuana
Roses—'Benzedrine' (brand of amphetamine sulfate,
    Smith Kline & French Laboratories) tablets

Sam—Federal narcotic agents

Satch cotton—cotton used to strain narcotics before injection

Scat—heroin

Score—to purchase drugs

Seggy—'Seconal' (brand of secobarbital, Eli Lilly and Company) capsules

Shooting gallery—a place where narcotic addicts inject drugs

Shoot up—to inject drugs

Slammed—in jail

Sniff—to sniff narcotics (usually heroin or cocaine) through the nose

Snow—cocaine

Speedball—an injection which combines a stimulant and depressant —often cocaine mixed with morphine or heroin

Spike—the needle used for injecting drugs

Square—a non-addict

Star dust—cocaine

Stash—a cache of narcotics

Stick—a marihuana cigarette

Stuff—narcotics

Sugar—powdered narcotics

Swingman—a drug supplier

Texas tea—marihuana

Thoroughbred—a high-type hustler who sells pure narcotics

Tooies—'Tuinal' (brand of amobarbital sodium and secobarbital sodium, Eli Lilly and Company) capsules

Trip, tripping—being "high" on hallucinogens, particularly LSD

Truck drivers—amphetamine

Turkey—a capsule purported to be narcotic but filled with a non-narcotic substance

Turned off—withdrawn from drugs

Turned on—under the influence of drugs

Uncle—Federal narcotic agent

Wake-ups—amphetamine

Washed up—withdrawn from drugs

Wasted—under the influence of drugs

Weed—marihuana

Weed-head—marihuana user

Weekend habit—a small, irregular drug habit

Whiskers—Federal narcotic agents

Whites—amphetamine sulfate tablets

White stuff—morphine

Works—the equipment for injecting drugs

Yellow-jackets—'Nembutal' (brand of pentobarbital, Abbott Laboratories) capsules (solid yellow)